WAY OUT IN IDAHO

WAY OUT IN IDAHO

A Celebration of Songs and Stories
Compiled with an Introduction
by Rosalie Sorrels

Foreword by Robert McCarl

Confluence Press, Inc.
in association with
The Idaho Commission on the Arts
Lewiston/Boise 1991

Printed in the United States of America
First Edition

ISBN 0-917652-83-5 (Paper)
Library of Congress Card Number
90-083710

Publication of this book is made possible, in part, by
generous grants from the Idaho Humanities Council and the Idaho
Centennial Commission.

Published by: Distributed to the trade by:
Confluence Press, Inc.   National Book Network
Lewis-Clark State College   4720-A Boston Way
8th Avenue and 6th Street   Lanham, Maryland 20706
Lewiston, Idaho 83501

Portrait Photographs: Michael Cordell
Musical Notation: John Cochrane, Kathy Pengelly, Professor James Murphy
and Idaho Commission on the Arts, Boise, Idaho 83720

Idaho Commission on the Arts / 304 West State / Boise, Idaho 83720

Front Cover Photograph Courtesy of the
Idaho State Historical Society
"Around the campfire in Landore (sic) about 1912."

To the people of Idaho

TABLE OF CONTENTS

❖❖❖
FOREWORD

The book that you hold in your hands represents literally years of planning, travel, research, and effort on the part of thousands of people in Idaho. Funded by the Idaho Centennial Commission through a grant to the Idaho Commission on the Arts, the Idaho Folk Song Project officially began in July of 1987 as the first statewide activity to celebrate Idaho's 1990 Statehood Centennial. The project's primary goal was to begin the process of collecting and building an archive of folk songs and music sung and played by the people of Idaho as they went about their daily lives before and during the course of the last century. We also wanted to compile a representative selection of Idaho folk songs to publish in book form. Perhaps most importantly, we wanted to stimulate the interest of our state's people in the history of their own communities and to encourage these communities to seek out their own singers, songwriters, and storytellers. In other words, we wanted to create a large scale public folklore project devoted to folk song and folk music: something that had not been done since Vardis Fisher and the other state guidebook writers of the Works Progress Administration attempted to capture the regional cultures of our nation back in the 1930's.

In order to create a model project, we asked Rosalie Sorrels to set aside her concert schedule and head a project team that traveled to Idaho communities, both large and small, where she presented some thirty concerts and "song swaps." The response was both immediate and enthusiastic. "We collected enough material to fill several volumes," Rosalie reported, "and it was only with great difficulty that we selected the individual songs that make up this book. The finished product," Rosalie emphasized, "is only suggestive of our state's various regions and the diversity of our people in terms of their occupations and backgrounds."

"Folk songs and stories come directly from the people," Rosalie concluded, "and they flesh out the bare bones and add a human element to the historical record. They tell us about the kind of people who lived here before us, and they also reflect our current concerns and their continuity with the past." In this sense, through their willingness and eagerness to support Rosalie in her concerts, song swaps, and fieldwork, it is really the people of Idaho who created this book. Someone once defined folklore as "necessary knowledge made attractive." And in its simplicity, that's a pretty good definition. Reading through *Way Out in Idaho* we can see that definition expressed in a variety of ways. The joy of Idaho's natural beauty and the humor of a child's nonsense rhyme, for example, contrast sharply with the racism of an ethnic epithet or the sexism of a descriptive phrase. Consequently, we must keep in mind that folk material provides us with verbal and musical windows into the feelings, sentiments, and fears of people. We must understand both the negative and the positive aspects of our collective experiences so that we can bring those differences between ethnic groups, men and women, and people who follow various trades, out into the open. The folk songs contained in this book are still being sung, and in their blending of humor, anger, and nonsense they define a place that is irreducible to any single voice or point of view. They remind us that we share universal human values, that in the essentials of what constitutes human conduct we differ very little. We all know what defines kindness, generosity, friendship, and love.

Perhaps needless to say, in completing this phase of our project, we have encountered any number of difficulties. The logistical problems of touring a group in a state as geographically diverse as Idaho, for example, are not small. Certainly Rosalie Sorrels and her "troupe"—Jean Terra (Project Manager), John Pisano (Sound and Accompaniment), and Gary Grimm and Katy Flanagan (Multi-Media Background)—deserve particular recognition for their perseverance and patience. Not long after this group of intrepid travelers gave its last performance in Boise on April 24, 1988, the project nearly met with tragedy. Before Rosalie and Jean could complete the shaping and final editing of the manuscript, Rosalie was hospitalized with a brain aneurysm. The story made national news. And for weeks the people of Idaho and friends throughout the nation prayed for Rosalie's recovery. Happily, perhaps even miraculously, Rosalie has fully recovered now and is at work on two new albums. Without her rugged Idaho constitution and generous help in the months that followed, this book may never have materialized at all. Rosalie's commitment to this project has resulted in this publication. As a folklorist and a performer, she has enriched our lives for the last thirty years. I know I join the people of her native state in saying how immeasurably much she means to us all.

It was Rosalie, of course, who first pointed out the necessity of adding another important dimension to this book: its organization and design. At her suggestion, we have created the book to be both read *and* used—stretched out flat, propped up on the piano and sung to. In addition to songs sent in to the project and those sung by people at the many song swaps held during the collection phase of the project, the book also includes songs that Rosalie has sung for years. But the project really only begins here. We will house all the collected material in a folk song archive so that future researchers can continue to collect and annotate the traditional songs and music of our state. Any number of academic and popular books could easily follow the publication of *Way Out in Idaho*. All of us hope that will be the case.

Rosalie has included two kinds of songs in this book: the first are individually composed and attributed lyrics sung to popular tunes. These are clearly identified in Rosalie's introductions to the selections. The second are either traditional or unique tunes that are original or little known and taken from the individual performance of the composer or the contributor. Kathy Pengelly in Eugene, Oregon, and John Cochrane from the More's Creek String Band wrote the lead sheets. Professor Jim Murphy transcribed the music onto computer software for publication through the cooperation of the Music Department at the College of Idaho. Michael Cordell of Boise created the photographic portraits of the individual contributors. We have supplemented these with photos from the Idaho

Historical Society, Rosalie's personal collection, and other sources listed in the captions. Archie Green provided invaluable assistance by reading and criticizing drafts of the manuscript. Shannon Hack typed and retyped the manuscript countless numbers of times. Without her tireless efforts, this collection of songs would never have become a book.

Finally, as a public folklorist, I would like to add a personal note. Much of what I do as the Folk Arts Director in Idaho is "culture-specific." For example, I work with the five tribes on apprenticeship grants, with the Hispanic community on survey work, and so on. The Idaho Folk Song Project gave me an opportunity to look over Rosalie's shoulder and see a broad picture (both past and present) of the complex and rich cultures of our state. I can think of no better way to serve the people of Idaho and to celebrate our various reactions to this remarkable place than to appreciate the songs, stories, and concerns contained in this book.

—*Robert McCarl*
Folk Arts Director
Idaho Commission on the Arts

❖❖❖
ACKNOWLEDGEMENTS

Thanks must go, of course, to the Idaho Centennial Commission for selecting the Idaho Folk Song Project as its first statewide project to celebrate Idaho's 1990 Centennial; and to the Idaho Commission on the Arts for administering the project. Both of these commissions, their members and their staffs, gave us their patience and confidence.

Particular thanks must go to the local arts organizations, chambers of commerce, folk song societies, and other local groups who sponsored the song swaps we held in communities throughout Idaho. Their help was essential to the success of our programs.

But our deepest gratitude goes to the thousands of Idaho people who helped make this songbook happen: to those who came to the song swaps and especially to those who sang their songs and told their stories, as well as those others who sent us material and provided us with leads. To those who invited us into their homes, we also offer special thanks—there's no warmer hospitality than that of Idahoans. To those who have written (and are still writing!) just to express their appreciation for the Folk Song Project and to encourage and support our efforts, we extend our continued thanks.

To list all the names of the people who had a part in the creation of this book would take another couple of volumes, but you all know who you are. And we thank you from the bottom of our hearts. It has been a wonderful experience getting to know so many extraordinary people.

—Rosalie Sorrels and Jean Terra

The Rev. Robert Stanton Stringfellow, the Buckskin Parson.
(Photograph courtesy of Rosalie Sorrels)

EE-DA-HOW

Over the hills there is sunshine,
I see their sunlit crest.
No winter with frost and snow is there,
No gloomy days, no clouds of despair,
And all is eternal rest.

Over the hills there is sunshine,
And I hear the happy song,
Of souls grown weary of sadness here,
Of crosses and care, of doubts and of fear,
Now gladden that glorious throng.

Over the hills there is sunshine;
O may I fall asleep
Late in some slumberous afternoon,
When lengthening shadows creep,
And may I wake in that brighter land
That the golden sunshine fills,
A land where the clouds are never seen,
Far over the shining hills.

—Canon Stringfellow

❖❖❖
INTRODUCTION

Ever since I was a little girl, I've believed that the name of my state was taken from a Nez Perce phrase that meant "See how the morning sun is shining on the mountains." When I have been on a long journey and I return in the morning, I say those words over and over to myself—calling back my grandmothers and grandfathers, calling back faces and rooms, places and times so long gone by. That's what folklore is— the homemade, hand-wrought stuff of memory— not history, but color—the blood and breath of then and now.

I know that scholars have repeatedly proven "Idaho" is not an Indian word, but "the romance that lies in her name" is a good story. And if it is not true, it oughta be.

My Grandfather Stringfellow came from Culpepper County, Virginia. He was an Episcopal Missionary who crossed the badlands alone and took on the West. On June 30, 1903, he married Rosalie Cope in Salt Lake City at St. Paul's. Then, off they went to live in tents and lodges in Montana and Idaho, there to connect the souls they encountered to God.

My Grandmother Rosalie, who came from a journalistic family in eastern Canada, bore four sons out in the wilds of the West. My dad, Walter Pendleton Stringfellow, was born in Helena, Montana. When he grew up he was, for a while, the materials engineer for the Idaho State Highway Department, and he helped build roads to connect the people of Idaho, north to south, east to west. Now I have retraced all those paths on my mission to collect songs and stories from all over Idaho and to help connect the people of this young western state to their past.

I began this recent odyssey as a way of celebrating Idaho's 100th birthday as a state. With the support of an Idaho Centennial Commission grant to the Idaho Commission on the Arts and the help of my project director and long-time friend, Jean Terra, our journey began. First, Jean did all the bookings, sending out endless letters and promotional materials. Next, we enlisted the talents of John Pisano (known to most Idaho musicians as "Johnny Shoes"). John went with us everywhere . . . setting up the sound and recording equipment for me and the people who sang at our song swaps . . . recording private sessions with those who were too shy to sing in front of a big group or who lived too far away to make it to a concert. In addition, John played a lot of pretty mandolin licks behind me during appearances.

Part of the time, Gary Grimm and Katy Flanagan of Mountain Visions also accompanied us. Gary and Katy created a stunning multi-projector visual display from my family photographs to go with the concerts. We carefully chose each picture, story, or song in the program to remind the people of Idaho of their own family treasures.

And treasures they are . . . those pictures, stories, songs, and bits of life folded away in trunks and pockets of memory . . . more powerful and lasting than the gold so many came here to find. Civilizations have crumbled while a little pipe tune or a lullaby has sung on through centuries, doing its work, sewing together the fabric of life.

To me, music is the strongest bond of all because when people need to come together, they sing a common song. When we make a union, when we unite to defend ourselves or to protest injustice, we reach back for comfort to the songs that are familiar: "I had a terror since September, I could tell to none; and so I sing, as the boy does by the burying ground, because I am afraid," Emily Dickinson once wrote in a letter to her editor.

One half-forgotten lullaby, learned years and years ago in the safe arms of a loving parent, can save your life. It can give you the strength to continue against all odds.

The first thing I learned about this state during our travels was that it is exotic. Our population is as varied as our geography. One of our first stops, for example, was Buhl in Twin Falls County, not far from the city of Twin Falls. We arrived midday at the senior center where we were met by Matilda Machacek, a member of that county's Czechoslovakian community. Matilda and several others of Czech descent wore their traditional costumes and organized a delightful afternoon for us. They had prepared a feast that included *Kolace* (a pastry) and the best strudel I have ever tasted. Some of the children danced for us, a young woman sang an old song in a lovely soprano voice, and people from neighboring towns also came in to sing. My favorite part of the afternoon was when a group of about sixteen women sang a Czechoslovakian song that expressed the exact purpose of our project:

TA NAŠE PÍSNIČKA ČESKÁ
(Our Czech Song)

Our pretty Czech songs
Are like those precious pearls
Lovingly strung on a string,
There's much beauty in them
And it's a great sin
They should be so oppressed.
This is our beautiful Czech song
So lovely, so lovely begun,
Just like a flower in the meadow
Grew our beautiful song, you know.
If ever our song becomes lost
Then nothing else will remain.
Should it once perish, all else with it will vanish.
Even we no more then will live.

Our journey throughout Idaho was fascinating. We stopped in Hailey for a song swap at Sonja Tarnay's bed and breakfast spot—elegantly furnished with things from bygone days. Johnny Shoes played his mandolin for me in the shadow of the Devil's Bedstead on the way to Salmon. We traveled to Kamiah, with its many artists, and took a side trip up and up precipitous back roads to visit Stella Hendren, who has a collection of 100,000 songs and makes the best cherry pie I have had in years. We also went to Kooskia and visited Blanche Cowger, who contributed many songs to this collection—and sang them to us in a lovely husky voice, inviting in the neighbors for an afternoon gathering.

Grangeville brought us together with John Carrey, whom we visited later at his hometown of Riggins. He told us tales of the Townsend Plan, of his friendships with Polly Bemis, Sylvan Hart, and Idaho Jack, a blind fiddler whose songs you'll find in this collection.

We traveled to the top of the panhandle—to Bonners Ferry, Coeur d'Alene, and Sandpoint—and went 'round to St. Maries where we met Leila Olin. It was her 90th birthday. And she invited us in and gave us an IWW song, "50,000 Lumberjacks."

Wallace was a treat. I performed in a theater run by the Sixth Street Players. The place was jammed. I think the many people who came to participate could have sung all night. And we heard tales of mine disasters and shady ladies, songs for fun and songs to celebrate years of hardship and hanging on. We stayed in the Jameson Hotel and had some of the world's best bread pudding for breakfast.

Our travels took our cast to Rexburg and Preston, to Idaho Falls and to Pocatello. I sang in an old movie theater, a church, a museum, a university, and a coffeehouse. The coffeehouse was U.S. Bert's Corner Cup in Pocatello, run by Bert and Sharon, who make you feel as if you are in their living room, swapping songs and stories with old friends. We heard Mormon songs on the eastern side of the state and songs of farmers and their families. We heard stories of trains and old lost souls.

At Fort Hall I visited Bonnie Teton and saw the Shoshone-Bannock Museum there. Later, I went back for a huge gathering and stayed all night to listen to the awe-inspiring music of at least forty drums. (A "drum" is the name for a group of musicians who play drums and flute and sing. Each drum is different. The Fort Hall gathering brings drums from as far away as Alaska, Canada, New Mexico, and Arizona.) Everyone wore festive traditional clothing—handmade buckskins with intricate beading, porcupine quill work, headgear with feathers and horse hair. I met an old woman who remembered my grandfather when he had been the pastor there. It was an unforgettable night.

We visited St. Gertrude's Priory at Cottonwood and saw Polly Bemis's gold work and learned more about the Chinese. In Nampa, we attended the Cinco de Mayo celebration and discovered that Idaho's Hispanic population is *very* large and growing. There is a community of Finns near McCall. Greeks, Welsh, Irish, Scots—they all brought songs and stories to enrich our state. And the Basques . . . I was born in Boise and grew up with my Basque friends dancing and making so much music that I almost took it for granted. To fully understand how unique Basque music is, as a young woman I had to go to California. At a folklore conference at UCLA I heard grown-up people with Ph.D.s yell at each other all night about the origins of Basque culture and language. Some said the language was probably Celtic in the beginning; another suggested that maybe it was Hasidic, and one thought it was Arabic. Years ago, however, a Basque friend of my mother's told me it was the language spoken in Paradise. And that's good enough for me.

But the best part of our musical tour through Idaho did not come to an end at our last concert in Boise's Little Theater. And it will not come to an end. Folk music is alive and well. The celebrations, such as the Basque Jaialdi, the Mexican Cinco de Mayo celebration, the Greek Glendi, the annual Fort Hall Pow Wow, and others teach us how rich and various we are.

We still host one of the best known old-time fiddle contests in the United States at Weiser, where I met Blaine Stubblefield, the founder of that event, almost forty years ago when he first sang me *Way Out in Idaho*, "A-workin' on the narrow gauge way out in Idaho . . ."

It would take years to get around to all the songs that are alive in our communities, and by the time we got to every one, the song would have changed. We have tried to bring back some of the old songs and corral the points of view of our various contemporary singers; in some cases even without the music. I have included poems and stories and a few recipes because I know that if you just say "How do you do?" and shake hands with someone, you haven't really met. But if you sing together, dance together, break bread together, and share memories, you must come to be friends.

Here in this collection we can come together as friends. *Way Out in Idaho* is not a scholarly examination of our folk heritage, but a personal observation of the people of Idaho and the human legacy we have accrued in our short sojourn in this beautiful place. Here are old treasures, unique to us, but here, too, are common songs found everywhere. I have also included some new songs to remind us that our tradition continues, and I hope that every community will be inspired to dig around, find its own treasures, and make its own books and archives. These songs, stories, poems, bits and pieces are our patchwork of life. I thank the people of Idaho who have not only provided me with the material for this book but helped me stitch it together.

—Rosalie Sorrels
Boise, Idaho 1990

The 'crew,' left to right: Katy Flanagan, Gary Grimm, Rosalie Sorrels, John Pisano, Jean Terra. . . .
Good company, good times, and some real contact with the heart and soul of Idaho were the common
experiences we shared as we traveled the state from side to side and end to end. It was a true privilege to
work with such talented and good hearted people. (Photo courtesy of Michael Cordell)

Ellen Moses carrying wood. (Photographer: Hutchison. Nez Perce Photographs from Nez Perce National Historical Park. Spalding, Idaho)

WE WERE ALWAYS HERE

THE NATIVE PEOPLE OF IDAHO

We come from no country, as have the whites.
We were always here.
Nature placed us in this land of ours.
Yellow Wolf
Nez Perce leader

The native people of Idaho, like those who came later and those who continue to reside here, express their diversity, spirit, and independence through their poetry and song. These sovereign people represent a variety of cultures, languages, and lifestyles that continues to flourish and grow today. Each nomadic band, extended family, and tribe had a traditional name for itself (often simply "the people") and a name given to it by those who first made contact with the original inhabitants of what is now Idaho. By simply examining the modern names used to describe Idaho's native people, we begin to unravel some of the traditional histories these people maintain about themselves. We also reveal some of our misconceptions about native people.

Coeur d'Alene *means "heart of an awl," which seems to imply "hard-hearted." This is a poorly conceived designation for a people who lived in peace for hundreds of years prior to the coming of the Blackrobes and who built a beautiful church at Cataldo to please them and to honor the Creator. They call themselves Schee-chue-umsh, which means "ones*

found here" and that makes a lot more sense.

Nez Perce *is a name the French trappers brought into the region. It means "pierced nose," but this tribe has never pierced their noses for ornamentation — although someone told me that they might have pierced the noses of their horses. I guess the trappers were just confused. The Nez Perce call themselves* Itse ye' ye (num) mamayats *or "Children of the Coyote." I have also been told that they called themselves Ne-Mee-Poo or simply "the people."*

The Shoshone *and* Bannock *people represent two large groups of nomadic bands who ranged throughout the region in search of food and in response to seasonal changes. The Shoshone people from the Fort Hall area referred to themselves as* Bohoque, *a term that Julian Steward and others suggest is derived from the word* bohovi *("sagebrush" plus* que *"on top of," or "butte"). The Bannock call themselves* Bana'kwut, *from their word for water.*

The southern Shoshone *and northern* Paiute *people on the Duck Valley Reservation also lived in small, extended families that ranged throughout the high desert plateaus of northern Californian and Nevada, southern Oregon, and Idaho. The Paiutes called themselves (according to Steward) Paviotso, and the western Shoshones used the term Newe. Although representing literally hundreds of nomadic groups and families, descendants of these original people continue to thrive as farmers and ranchers on the reservation.*

The Kootenai refer to themselves as Ktunagha, which means "putting something down." They are an inland, maritime people who continue to rely heavily upon fishing and hunting in the many northern lakes and rivers throughout northern Idaho, Montana, and British Columbia. As with other northwest tribes, both those on the coast and inland, the cycle of the salmon continues to exert a strong influence on the secular and spiritual lives of the Kootenai people.

Idaho's native heritage is indeed rich. But the reservation system has thrown together people who are unrelated to each other, and it continues to separate native people while providing them with land and resources of increasing value. It is important as we listen to the words and music of Idaho's Indian people to keep in mind that their traditions and customs provide all of us with an appreciation of how lives lived in cooperation with nature can insure our future.

—R.S.

❖❖❖

❖ *It is impossible to say where the first song or story originated in Idaho country. This literary account of Native American origin, from Eleanor Heady in her book* Sage Smoke: Tales of the Shoshoni-Bannock Indians *(Follett Publishing Company, 1973), provides a useful beginning.* —R.S.

HOW THE INDIANS GOT THEIR MUSIC

Long Ago when the Indians first came to Shoshoni country, they had no music, no songs, no tom-toms, no rattles, nor whistles.

In that time there was a hunter whose name was Gray Elk. One day he went walking in the hills, high among the rocks, looking for fat groundhogs for supper.

As Gray Elk walked along, a wind arose, stirring the dust around him and bending the aspens and sagebrush tops. The winds made a whispering tune, and Gray Elk began to hum. Farther up the hill, where the wind blew against the rocks and between the cracks in the ledges, he heard moaning and whistling. Gray Elk tried these sounds, too. Soon he was humming and singing as he walked along. He became so enchanted with the song he sang that he forgot all about hunting groundhogs and returned to camp empty-handed.

By this time he had put words to the song and sang as he walked:

> Breath of the mountains,
> Blow down the valleys,
> Bring joy to the people
> Who live by the river.

Gray Elk sang his song around the evening campfire. He taught it to the others who camped with him. Soon everyone sang:

> Breath of the mountains,
> Blow down the valleys,
> Blow rain to the lowlands
> And grass to the prairies.

Bright Star lived in the same camp by the river. One day she put her baby, Bluebird, in the *Kohon*, or cradleboard, and put it on her back. She picked up her sharp digging stick and buckskin bag and went out into the meadow to dig camas roots.

As she dug for the crisp white bulbs, she bent over the long grass. She heard the wind singing in the grass leaves. She began to hum a song to her baby, a lullaby:

> Hear the soft rustling,
> The sigh of the grass leaves,
> Singing to Bluebird,
> Singing a sleep song.

And the baby fell asleep on her back. When Bright Star's bag was filled to the top, she straightened and looked up into the aspen trees that bordered the meadow. The trees rustled in the breeze with a tiny tinkling tune. Bright Star listened. Then she sang with the aspens:

> *Breeze from the prairies,*
> *Leaves on the aspen*
> *Mingle together,*
> *Sing in the sunlight.*

Bright Star returned to her wickiup singing her two songs. That evening she sang them to the others around the campfire. Then, as darkness fell over the land, all the people sang the songs they had learned from the wind, the rocks, the trees, and the grass.

The next morning Brown Buffalo, the wisest man in the camp, came out of his tepee just as the sun came over the eastern mountains. He remembered the songs of the night before, and as a meadowlark trilled from the top of a tall sagebrush, he burst into song. So was born the "Hymn to the Morning," a prayer sent on the rays of the rising sun to the great Father of all, *Apa*. Since that time, the Shoshoni have started each day with this beautiful song.

Time passed, and the people added more songs, songs they learned from the birds, the breeze, the sighing pines, and the howling wind. They made drums of animal skins and rattles of dried animal stomachs. With these instruments they kept time to the music. They began to dance to the sounds, to stamp, to clap their hands. Now whenever Indians gather for a great festival, it is a time of much singing, dancing, and drumming.

And that is how the Indians found music.

The story is finished. The rat's tail dropped off, surely—surely.

❖❖❖

❖ *I found the following myth in a tabloid publication entitled* Idaho's Indians—Idaho's Heritage, *which was published by Idaho's five tribes in 1986. This story not only relates the origin of the Kootenai people, it also suggests their continued association with the inland waters of the interior northwest.* —R.S.

KOOTENAI MYTH

In the beginning before there were people in the world, the Kootenai legend tells of a sea monster who escaped from the lakes of Canada and worked his way into the Kootenai River feasting on the birds along the way. The treachery of this monster caused all the remaining birds and animals to try to stop the devil beast. Although a flock of woodpeckers headed him off briefly, they were not able to hold the monster. A huge and powerful bird then flew ahead knocking down pieces of surrounding mountains until the river passage was blocked.

Hearing that the monster has been headed off, Coyote and his friend Wolf set off to kill the beast. Soon Wolf became tired and gave his clothing, spear, and shield to Coyote who went on ahead. But Coyote didn't have the courage to kill him when he found the monster. Fortunately, Wolf caught up and killed the beast for all the animals.

The Woodpecker, who was headman for the animals, then cut-up the monster freeing all the birds inside. He threw the pieces around the countryside and where the white meat fell there were white men. The yellow pieces became oriental people and the blood became the proud, brave Indians.

Kootenai woman crossing river. (Photograph courtesy of Bonner County Historical Society)

Lawrence Aripa holding photograph of his father and mother: Stanislaw and Mary Aripa. (Photo courtesy of Michael Cordell)

❖ *Lawrence Aripa, besides being a fine Idaho artist, has a smoke shop on the Coeur d'Alene reservation near Plummer. I went to visit him there and listened to his tale of Coyote and the Magical Logs. Lawrence's* *shop is a warm room filled with his art, the art of his friends, and mementos of a rich past — a perfect room for tale-telling.*
— R.S.

COYOTE STORY
By Lawrence Aripa

I've been here all my life except for the time I went to Denver. Then, of course, I was in the Navy in the World War II. In the beginning I was in the South Atlantic, and then I was moved to the South Pacific, then to the Philippines. I was in for about three years . . . I enlisted when I was seventeen. Everything was strange to me, but it was a learning experience. I got to see a lot of places and was able to come back and tell the kids the things that I had seen. Most of all it made me appreciate what I have here.

This story was told to me by my great grandmother, who was from the Spokane Tribe. And she, of course, could speak the Coeur d'Alene language as well. She had heard it from my grandfather's mother, who passed away before I knew her. My great grandmother from my grandmother's side learned the story from the Coeur d'Alene people . . . . She was quite a storyteller and she always told us stories not only from the Spokane Tribe but from the Coeur d'Alene Tribe as well. She was always very interesting.

The story that I am going to tell is about the coyote. It kind of fits in with the old saying that the grass is always greener on the other side. (I've always liked the story because it combines the humans with the animals.) All of the coyote stories that were told a long time ago always had a moral to them and so, the stories always had a lesson for the younger people. This particular story took place up in the St. Joe River and that is where the Coeur d'Alene people lived, part of them.

It happened that one day the coyote was strolling along the river really enjoying himself. He was eating what he could find, small bits of animals and different things. But he wasn't getting enough.

As he went up the river, all of a sudden, he stopped and high up on the mountain across the river, he saw a real nice green spot. The sun was shining on it and it looked like a great place for things to live. He knew that because of the green vegetation there would be many animals and he could eat. He tried to find a way to get across the river.

Old Lady Mole came by and looked at him and said, "What are you doing? You crazy coyote! I see you running up and down the bank like you're puzzled."

He says, "Well, I want to get across the river but I can't do it."

So Old Lady Mole told him, "You should have learned to swim a long time ago when you were young and you would be able to swim anytime you wanted." She said, "You'd better learn."

He said, "No. I don't have to learn. I can find other ways to get across."

She told him, "If you want to cross the river, then you go downstream about five miles. There's a shallow place where you can wade across."

He said, "No, I'm going to get across here somehow."

She told him to be careful, "You always get yourself in trouble by doing something you don't know anything about. So you be careful. And you shouldn't be so lazy, go down where it's shallow."

Again he said, no, so she left him and said, "I warned you anyway." She left and he started up the river.

He was going and enjoying himself and at the same time yearning to get across to that beautiful green spot. As he was looking, trying to figure a way to get across, all of a sudden he heard a human's voice, so he stopped to listen and way off in the distance he heard, *sh ste'wish a lee, tsts'e te'wish a lee.* He wondered, "What is that?" He knew the Indian language, so he listened again and he said, "That means *log go apart, log come back.* What does that mean?" He was puzzled. He kept going up the bank of the river. He came to a lot of brush and the voice was stronger: *sh ste'wish a lee, tsts'e te'wish a lee* So then he took the brush apart and there on the river was a little boy standing on two logs. He would look down at the logs and sing: *sh ste'wish a lee,* and the logs would go apart; he

7

would sing *tsts'e te'wish a lee'* and the logs would slowly come back together. As the logs went back and forth, the boy was moving.

So the coyote thought, "Ah, there's how I'll get across. I'll use his magic logs to get across the river. Then I can go to that green spot." Then he thought, "I will have to figure out a way to get that boy away from those logs."

So he went back into the brush and started to holler like he was in trouble. He shouted, "Help! Help! I need help!" He spoke in the Indian language.

The boy heard it and he thought, "Well, it's something else—it's none of my business." He kept on with the logs singing, *sh ste'wish a lee', tsts'e te'wish a lee'.* So the logs kept going back and forth. The coyote kept on hollering and shouting, asking for help. Finally, the boy turned the logs and headed for shore. When he got to the shore, he jumped off the logs and ran up the bank and started to look for where the voice came from.

In the meantime, the coyote ran over and jumped on the logs and he says, "Now, if I can only remember the words . . . ." He looked down at the logs and sang *sh ste'wish a lee'.* Sure enough, the logs started to part. When the logs got out to where his legs were stretched, he sang *tsts'e te'wish a lee'* and they came back together. He started to move out on the river. He says, "Now, I can make it. Now I can get to that green spot." He started to sing the tune again, and the logs minded him and would go back and forth. He said to himself that this is great. He thought to himself that I got to get there faster, so he started singing faster: *sh ste'wish a lee', tsts'e te' wish a lee'.* The logs started going back and forth faster and faster. He was moving faster.

Then all of a sudden the boy came back to the edge of the river and he shouted, "What are you doing? What are you doing with my logs?"

The coyote turned to him and said, "I am taking your logs and I am going to keep them. These are magic logs and I like them." He turned away from the boy and said to himself, "Now I can get across, now I can get to the green spot." He thought to himself, "To heck with the boy. I don't have to pay any attention to him now." So then he went back to the logs and sang *sh ste'wish a lee'.* The logs started to part. All of a sudden he forgot the other word: *tsts'e te'wish a*

lee'; the logs were getting wider and wider and his legs stretched and they kept going and his legs kept getting longer until finally his legs couldn't stretch anymore. He couldn't remember the words to get him back. He fell into the river and drowned.

So his body floated down river. His body caught on a piece of underbrush. He got hooked there and that's where his body laid . . . .

Old Lady Mole kept searching and searching. "I know that coyote is around somewhere, I have to find him." She kept looking for months. Finally, she found him hooked on the brush, and so she took his bones and put them on the bank, and then she went into her magic song. She sang her favorite song, jumped over the coyote three times, and he came back to life.

He stretched his arms and looked up and said, "I've been asleep a long time. Thank you for letting me sleep."

Old Lady Mole said, "Asleep! You were gone, you were in the land beyond, you were not here."

He says, "No, I was asleep."

She says, "What are you doing then?"

He said, "I'm going to that green spot on the mountain."

She says, "You foolish, foolish coyote. You have to learn that you should not do anything that you are not familiar with, and you should not use the magic and power of other people, and you should listen when you get advice. You should listen to what your elders tell you. You will never change. You should learn a lesson from this."

Mrs. Lawyer winnowing grain. (Photo courtesy of Idaho State Historical Society)

Phil George is a poet from the Joseph Band of the Nez Perce Tribe. I selected this poem and inserted it here because of Phil's ability to capture both the importance of storytelling and the sacredness of the creative act in native cultures. —Robert McCarl

SEASON FOR GRANDMOTHERS
By Phil George

Falling snow silences summer stories;
Grandmother's fire, Grandmother's lodge,
Resting content in the center,

Ancient languages pantomime hands
Your own people's creation in story and song,
Not one word, not one movement, must you miss.

Solemn tunes, shadows on the tepee wall,
Tomorrow's proof of living past,
Soothing moments—sleep comes soon.

Under her arms, winter warmth;
Expecting you, uninvited she sleeps,
Now mothers, fathers are not important,

This, the white moon of legends and dreams,
Never too old for memories, loving
Season of Grandmothers.

Nez Perce Men on Clearwater River. (Photo courtesy of National Park Service, Nez Perce National Historical Park)

❖*Mr. Charlie Kipp of Kooskia came to our song swap in Kamiah and kindly gave us the following description of fishing on the Clearwater River. Stories and accounts like his provide an important link between the life ways of the past and the environmental traditions of modern Indian life.*

FISHING ON THE CLEARWATER RIVER
By Charles Kipp

I am now eighty-three years of age and reside at Kooskia, Idaho. I am a member of the Nez Perce Tribe of Idaho. From about the age of two or three I was raised by my grandparents and I have lived in this area most of my life.

In my earlier years I fished in the Clearwater River and many of its tributaries. I am familiar with the old style of fishing from canoes and have fished that way myself many times.

At one time I had a dug out canoe that was about twenty-two feet long. I sold that canoe to Spalding Park. When I first obtained the canoe, I used to fill it with water near my house for my children to play in, and they did—a lot.

There was a lady from this area named Juliana Scott who knew how to make canoes and could instruct other people on how to make them. She used to walk up the river, maybe twenty-five to thirty miles. She would walk through the woods looking at big cedar trees until she found one that was right. Then she would tell the men how to cut it down, and, once it was down, how to shape the canoe. They would cut the outside angles first. Then they would rough out the inside by cutting and burning. The inside was smoothed by rocks. She had three canoes of her own. I used to go help this lady with her work and help her garden when I was about thirteen or fourteen years old. She must have been about forty years old then. She quit making canoes about 1912 or 1913.

Once a person had a canoe, he needed other things to go fishing. We would make a metal frame and weave wire around it until it looked like a basket. This would go in the middle of the canoe and would be wired to the sides, so that it wouldn't tip over. Then we would get pitch-wood and cut it up like kindling. Some would go in the front and some in the back of the canoe for balance. Shavings from this wood would go in the bottom of the basket, and then it would be filled with wood and we were ready to make our run.

There would be a man in front and a man in back of the canoe. Bill Parsons used to be my fishing partner. Each man had a pole about fifteen feet long. If the canoe was made right, it was easy to move, even upstream. They were designed to go up and over riffles. The nose went up and they didn't go deep in the water.

When we got to a good place we would start our run. The fire would be lit, and the flames would go up about four feet high. We would start about 10:30/11:00 p.m.—because that's when the fish start moving. The canoe would be turned sideways in the river and would be allowed to drift downstream for about 250 feet. This was one run. With the fire you could see all the fish out twenty to twenty-five feet.

It was important to be very quiet. If you put your head underwater and hit two rocks together, it sounds loud. Salmon can hear sounds like that if you bump the side of the boat and talk. There are several kinds of spears that were used out of the canoe.

One kind used a pole about fifteen feet long that had a sharp point on one end. On this same end, two strips of wood were attached to the side of the pole, and they extended beyond the sharp end of the pole. At the ends of these two strips of wood, sharp points were placed that pointed toward each other and a little back toward the pointed end of the spear. In the old days, these were made of bone. More recently nails were used. The two strips of wood would move a little. When a salmon was hit with the sharp end of the pole, the two strips of wood would go around his sides and the hooks in them would go in so he could not escape. If the salmon turned, you had to turn the pole with him, or it would break. This was the old way.

There is another kind of spear that also uses a long pole. On this one, the end is rounded. Or something is placed over it so that it will slide over a fish. On this end, there are four grooves cut, equally spaced around the end. Then you take four big hooks that look like regular fish hooks. These go into the grooves so that the sharp end of the hooks point toward the rounded end of the pole. There is a string tied to each of the hooks, and these strings are all tied to the pole. When the spear is thrown or pushed at a salmon, one of the hooks will hit him. The hook comes out of the groove but is still attached to the pole so it can all be pulled in.

There was another way but I never saw it. It was a pole like a little javelin. It used a long pole. The sharp end had a head that had a hollow end that fit over the end of the pole. The end of the head was sharp, and it had a sharp point stick-ing out to the side like a barb. It was tied to the pole by a piece of rope so that when a fish was speared that head came off, but it was tied to the pole and could be pulled in.

A man rides his horse into the river, he has his hook on a pole and is ready to fish, and he sees a salmon. If he throws his spear at the salmon where he sees it, he will miss every time—the spear will go over the fish. So, for example, he looks and figures the salmon is in the water that is five feet deep. He imagines a line that is five feet away from the salmon toward him. Then he throws the spear at this line and he gets his salmon.

Another way to fish was in the winter time when there was ice in the river. One man would take a green pole with pitch on one end for light. He would go about six feet in front of the man with the spear and hold the light over the edge of the ice. They would go a mile or mile and a half and have lots of fish.

We also used to fish through a hole in the ice with bait and line.

Once I was with the lady who made canoes. She forgot her little hooks for trout. She had a shawl on and she pulled out a thread. She tied the thread together and put it on a line and put it in some riffles. She pulled trout right out onto the shore and I had to go catch them.

My father lived in this area. From 1890 to 1915, he used to see thirty, forty, fifty fish in one run in a canoe. I began fishing about 1912-1913 and fished until the 1930's. In later years I would see one or two—eleven was the highest.

Around 1913-1915 there were lots of salmon—Chinooks. Clear Creek had Dog Salmon. That was the only place I ever saw them. They were very big. If you got one, you had to cut the tail off to bleed it. About 1914-1915 was the last time I saw them.

I used to fish below Kamiah two or three miles, up about six miles above Kooskia.

I do not recall when the dam on the South Fork of the Clearwater went in.

In the South Fork at a place just above Kooskia, there used to be a fish trap clear across the river. They would take poles six to seven feet long that went across river. These were held by shorter poles placed upright with longer poles and extended so the water had to flow over it. The upriver side had thornbush woven like a basket. The fish would come up and jump over the trap into the thornbush basket on the up-river side.

People gathered here for this. There was a big celebration at the end of the run. When the run was over, the whole trap would be taken out.

There was a large camp at the confluence of the South Fork and the Middle Fork on the Kooskia side. It was too brushy for many camps on the other side. The camp crier divided up the fish. Most of it was dried. The people on the left side of the South Fork looking downstream went to Weippe for camas, then went home.

I don't know when that trap was last used. Jessie Spotted Eagle was a young man then.

Indian family with teepee — Hope, Idaho.(Photo courtesy of Bonner County Historical Society)

Nez Perce Drummers: Bill Stevens, Jr., Charlie Wilson, William "Bill" Johnson. Lapwai Grange Hall, 1950. (Nez Perce Photographs from the Nez Perce National Park, Spalding, Idaho)

The Nez Perce people in this area have a long history of trading, commerce, and statesmanship that began long before contact with Anglos. Once Whites entered their territory, however, the singers and drummers composed songs and chants that documented this contact. The willingness of people like Loran Olsen (a specialist in Nez Perce music) and Horace Axtell (a tribal elder, teacher, and drummer) to share this rich heritage is a testimony to the strength and beauty of this music and its ability to communicate complex issues in a lyrical style.

For example, as Loran Olsen notes in the Nez Perce Music Archives (Washington State University), "When old Chief Looking Glass and his warriors arrived singing this famous song, they interrupted the slick negotiations already well underway at the Walla Walla Treaty Council in 1855. Looking Glass and his companions railed against the other Nez Perce chiefs for their willingness to grant land to the invading Whites. His fellow chiefs overruled Looking Glass, however, and established a precedent for future concessions, agreements, and treaties, resulting in the loss of most of the traditional Nez Perce home ground. Also known as 'Chief Joseph's War Echo,' and 'War Leaders' Song,' this vigorous melody has become a virtual Nez Perce national anthem. In Sol Webb's recording, transcribed below, he sings the original as he learned it from his grandfather."—Robert McCarl

LEADERS' COUNCIL SONG

Traditional Nez Perce

As Loran Olsen reminds us, the 1855 Treaty was not ratified until 1863. Five years later, Chiefs Timothy, Lawyer, Jason, and Yutsinmáligkin traveled to Washington, D.C. to negotiate an amendment. On May 25, 1868, Yutsinmáligkin died of typhoid fever. He was buried the following day. Timothy, Lawyer, and Jason (along with M.G. Taylor, Commissioner of Indian Affairs) signed the amendment on August 13, 1868.

When the Nez Perce chiefs returned to Idaho, the people held a feast in memory of Yutsinmáligkin at Kamiah. It was there that Chief Isk'utim sang this ancient Nez Perce song to honor his dear friend. The names of these two chiefs, Isk'utim and Yutsinmáligkin, frequently appear together in official documents in connection with meetings and councils in the 1850's and 1860's.

—Robert McCarl

SONG FOR YUTSINMÁLIGKIN

Akámkinikai hiwíhinatatúm.
Hiwya hálxpawin tímas hitsém.
Imámtsitewes tsíqin
Kunk'u halxpáwin tímas hiwyátsem.

Way above, a message travels
Continually, the Sunday Book reports.
You hear yourself speaking this truth
Forever, as foretold in the Sabbath Book.

Horace Axtell is a great Nez Perce teacher who continues to pass on to the next generation (and even seriously interested outsiders) the customs and beliefs of his native tradition. (Photo courtesy of Michael Cordell)

Rosphine Coby is a Shoshone-Bannock woman who was raised by her grandparents on the Fort Hall Indian Reservation. She is a mother, teacher, student, artist, and poet. Her poems are receiving an increasing amount of attention from editors in the Northwest. At Fort Hall, Rosphine coordinates the Writing to Read lab for grades K-12. (Photo courtesy of Michael Cordell)

. . . The poem entitled "Grandma" is dedicated to the woman who has guided my eyes into the spiritual world of beauty.

My grandma, Nancy Horn, passed on several years ago. She taught me that life has a special place for me. Her spiritual guidance taught me that everything is alive and everything has a spirit. She taught me to see the beauty in nature and even to touch the breath of God.

This poem begins with my grandma on her death bed at the hospital. Throughout the ordeal I sat and evaluated what life offered her. I knew a lot of anger was within me, and with all these feelings inside, I put my thoughts into perspective and wrote this poem. It reflects my sadness, but from all this sadness inside, I was able to grasp life again and to see the beauty. I can still see my grandma's beauty within the cottonwood trees, the sagebrush, and the willows, because she loved nature so much.

The poem itself is very emotional for me. It was hard to write. It took me approximately three months to complete, but it expresses how I feel.

—Rosphine Coby

GRANDMA
By Rosphine Coby

As hours passed
as days passed,
as weeks passed,
I sat by your side.
Sometimes with my head bowed down.
I felt no movement from your body.
As I took your hand in mine,
I gave you warmth.
When you shut your eyes,
I will open my eyes.
And face the stern day.
When your dreams fade,
I will dream your dreams for you, Grandma.
When you no longer can lift your fingers,
I will stretch my fingers across the arid soil,
and build a new path.
When you no longer can walk,
I will finish walking in our sacred path, Grandma.
When there is no movement from your lips,
I will share your laughter in my dreams, Grandma.
When there is no movement in your heart,
my heart will surge toward the north,
toward the east,
toward the south,
toward the west.
Never beating alone,
Grandma,
never alone.

This fragment appeared in the 1986 publication that was funded by Idaho's five tribes: Idaho's Indians: Idaho's Heritage. *The legend explains the origins of all the tribes. The storyteller pays particular attention to how two different nomadic people, the Shoshones and the Paiutes, came to live together.*

—Robert McCarl

HOW THE SHOSHONES AND THE PAIUTES CAME TO LIVE TOGETHER

In the beginning, according to legend, Coyote left his homeland and traveled east across the ocean toward the rising sun. In distant lands he married and had many children. These were Indians. Planning to return home, he put all of them in a willow jug with a cork. He was warned not to open the jug before he reached his country of the Great Basin.

But hearing singing and beating of drums inside the basket and being curious, he took a peek when he reached this continent. The Indians jumped out and scattered and he was only able to close the jug in time to save two. He released them in the Great Basin country.

At first they began to fight, but Coyote kicked them apart and cautioned them: "You two are my children. You will be able to stand against the best and beat them."

This is the legend of how the Western Shoshone and Paiutes began as friends and populated the Great Basin of the United States . . . .

❖❖❖

This description of the Lemhi people who survived during the cold winters in the Salmon River country appeared in the Festival edition of the Sho-Ban News *published at Fort Hall, August 6, 1987.*

WINTER SURVIVAL REQUIRED EARLY START FOR LEMHI

Besides fishing for salmon, the Lemhi Shoshone once depended on roots and game to carry them through the cold Salmon winters.

Following their removal to the Fort Hall reservation in 1910, many families still made the long journey to Salmon to carry on the hunting, fishing, and root gathering traditions of the Lemhi people.

Tribal member Inez Evening remembers making the journey in the 1930s with her grandparents when she was about five years old.

They would travel to the Salmon River country in the early summer, when the bitter roots and blueberries were ready to be harvested.

Her family would dig the bitter root, peel the outer covering, and lay them out on a canvas to dry.

Some people boil bitter root and add it to soup bones. Others boil the root and put blueberries in it. By mid-July, the family was spearing salmon.

The Lemhi would spear the salmon before they spawned. The salmon was gutted by the men and dried by the women, the heads and tails were eaten right away so they wouldn't spoil.

In October, Evening's family traveled into the mountains to hunt for deer. The men would hunt and gut the deer and the women's job was to skin it.

The women would remove the sinew from the deer's body from the shoulders to the rump as they were skinning the deer.

The head of the deer was saved, since it had the brains used for tanning hides. Marrow in the legs was roasted and eaten.

The deer meat was thinly-sliced, draped over pieces of wood, and dried on tripods. A fire was built and the tripods were put all around the fire. The meat was left to dry for a couple of days.

The hair was scraped off the hides so they wouldn't be so heavy to carry back to Fort Hall. The rest of the tanning process was completed there.

Those hides that weren't scraped were used as mattresses. The ground was damp to sleep on and the deer hides kept them warm and dry, Evening said.

Their wagon would be loaded down with dried meat on their trip home in November.

Cora George, Evening's mother, said in the late 1800's some of the Lemhi would also travel to the Crow country and hunt for buffalo.

Evening also said there was a plant known as *toyahde*, which grew under the pine trees near springs in Salmon. This plant was used for tea.

There are two bands of the Lemhi; the band that lives near the river areas were known as the *agui duka*. Those who lived in the mountains were known as the *dtooku duka*. These people would hunt the mountain sheep or mountain goat.

Left: Water jug by Susie Shaw, ca. 1990. (Photo by Kelly Powell)
Right: Elsie Hall, Duck Valley. (Photo by Richard Hart)
Center: Left, Elizabeth Wilson; right, Agnes Moses digging camas at
Musselshell Meadow, 1965. (Nez Perce Photographs from
the Nez Perce National Park, Spalding, Idaho)

Just as the native people of Idaho documented and chronicled their contacts with Whites, Idaho settlers composed a variety of songs devoted to their perceptions of Indians. Although we may interpret some of these songs today as romantic or patronizing, we must keep in mind the cultural and historical contexts in which the songs were created. —Robert McCarl

❖❖❖

❖ When the Cataldo Mission was built in 1848, it was the center of a self-sufficient Coeur d'Alene village. The plans for the building were drawn by Father Ravalli, a Jesuit Missionary. His fellow clergymen and members of the Coeur d'Alene tribe constructed the building using only a broad axe, some pulleys, an auger, and a pocket knife. The church measures 90' x 40' and is one of the most beautiful buildings in Idaho. The poem was written several years ago when the Old Mission was being repainted. The author, L.H. Harry, lives less than six miles away. —R.S.

THE MISSION
By L. H. Harry

The oldest building standing
in the State of Idaho;
Is on a tiny knob of land
near the town of Cataldo.

It is a Jesuit Mission
that has stood the test of time
The question now is can it stand
the test of written rhyme.

This ancient wood structure
was raised by native hands.
Constructed with the simplest tools,
aided by the Father's plans.

The Indians learned to worship
and praise the Lord above.
The old Sacred Heart Mission
is the labor of their love.

Today it stands in prominence
and overlooks the vale.
That long ago was followed by
the Old Yellowstone Trail.

The Coeur d'Alenes have gone now
to the Indian reservation,
Once each year they pilgrimage
to that Sacred Old Foundation.

Cataldo Mission.(Photo courtesy of Idaho State Historical Society)

I learned this beautiful song from my grandmother, Mary Carrey Dustin, who lived for thirty years on the South Fork of the Salmon River, where I was born in 1914. Mary Carrey said she first heard the song when a young girl crossing the plains. She was at Long Creek, close to John Day area, when the Bannock War was on. She sang a lot when I was young. Our P. O. was Warren, Idaho.

—Johnny Carrey
Riggins, Idaho

LOST INDIAN

As Sung by Johnny Carrey

Once said a lost In-dian, "I once had a home in a far a-way land where the buf-fa-lo roam. Our old chief he made feast from the fat of the lay, But the steel of the white man has drove him a-way."

Once said a lost Indian, I once had a home
In a far away land where the buffalo roam
Our old chief he made feast from the fat of the lay
But the steel of the white man has drove him away.

Oh, I once had a mother to watch o'er my youth
And a father who taught me the precepts of truth
I once had a sweetheart but where is she now?
For the cold wind of death hangs low o'er her brow.

I once had a sister, the pride of the dale
And a brother whose features were sturdy and hale
Their spirits are vanished
They're cold in the clay
For the steel of the white man has swept them away.

Now soon I will answer the great spirit's call
In this far away land where the leaves never fall
On the radiant shore of the evergreen shade
Where the steel of the white man will never invade.

❖ *I have heard "Fallen Leaf," all of my life and seen it in many old song collections. These two versions are regionalized and specific to Idaho. One version of the song came from Stella Hendren in northern Idaho, and the other came from Mavin Sparks of Bennington in the southwestern part of the state. I included both versions (or "variants," as folklorists call them) not only because of their regional differences, but also to* *illustrate how folk songs continue to mix widely known tunes and lyrics with personal comment and variation. Stella says that the first variant of the song came from a cowboy who rode into the Two Bar Seventy camp on his blue horse, "Smoky," looking for work in the fall of 1887 or '88. He gave his name as Jim Stewart and said he was from Wyoming. Compare it to the version sung by Mavin Sparks, which turns the same song into an Indian romance.*

—R.S.

FALLEN LEAF

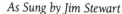

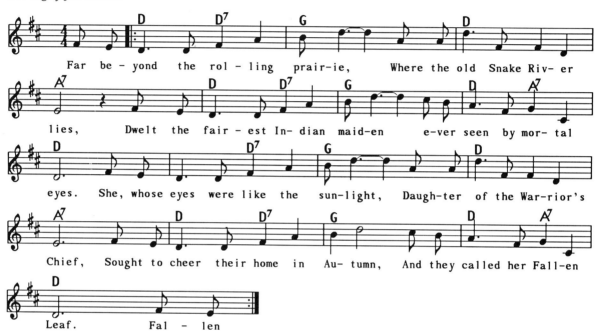

Far beyond the rolling prairie,
Where the old Snake River lies,
Dwelt the fairest Indian Maiden
Ever seen by mortal eyes.

She, whose eyes were like the sunlight,
Daughter of the Warrior's Chief,
Sought to cheer their home in Autumn,
And they called her Fallen Leaf.

CHORUS:
Fallen Leaf, the breezes whisper
Of the spirit's early flight,
And within that lonely wigwam,
There's a wail of woe to-night.

From far beyond the rolling prairie,
All alone one summer's day
Came a hunter, lone and weary,
To the Two Bar Seventy lay.

Weeks went by, but still he lingered,
"Gentle Fallen Leaf", he cried,
And with a smile of love she promised
Soon to be his woodland bride.

CHORUS:
One bright day this hunter wandered
On the Seventy range alone,
Long she watched and long she waited,
But his fate was never known.

With the summer days she faded,
With the autumn leaves she died
And they closed her eyes in slumber
Near the old Snake River side.

CHORUS:

❖ *Mavin Sparks tells us that another version of this song was sung by his Dad when he was riding the range in the summertime, which he did from the late 1890's until 1962. Mavin says, "From what I remember about this song as told by Dad, 'Falling Leaf' is the Girl of the Mists of the Indian Legend Shoshone Falls."*

Mavin also tells us of a "Salmon River" version of the song that "a fellow used to perform for his family and neighbors on the Camas Prairie at Fairfield and at Gooding."

—R.S.

FALLEN LEAF

As Sung by Mavin Sparks

Far out over the moun-tains o - ver the great di - vide waits a lone - ly In - dian maid- en for her war- rior home to ride. Long she's watched and long she's wait-ed There by old Snake Riv- er's side And the fal - ling leaves of au - tumn Can - not her sor- row hide. For in

Far out over the mountains
Over the great divide
Waits a lonely Indian maiden
For her warrior home to ride.

Long she's watched and long she's waited
There by Old Snake River's side
And the falling leaves of autumn
Cannot her sorrow hide.

For in the spring, her brave warrior
Had ridden across the prairie wide
Out o'er the snowy mountains
Far from old Snake River's side.

Then one day, a weary stranger
To her wigwam did ride
And told of the great battle
How her warrior brave had died.

Now in Falling Leaf's wigwam
There's a wail of woe tonight
There upon the lonely prairie
By old Snake River's side.

Sarah Pokibo Snipe, Bannock, in ceremonial dress. (Photo courtesy of Idaho State Historical Society)

❖ The Heart of the Appaloosa *is a contemporary song written by Fred Small, but we also heard it sung by many other Idahoans, including Opal Brooten in Wallace. We also heard it at the Coeur d'Alene song* swap. *Almost everyone swore they knew the person who had written it. In each case, it was a different person. This is the mark of a good song entering into the folk tradition and is a great compliment to the author.*

—R.S.

HEART OF THE APPALOOSA

Written by Fred Small

1. From the land of shoot-ing wa-ters to the peaks of the Coeur d'A-lenes, Thim-ble ber-ries in the for-est elk graz-ing on the plains, The peo-ple of the Coy - o-te made their camp a-long the streams Of the green Wal-low a Val-ley when fen-ces had no names.

2. And they bred a strain of hor-ses, the trea-sure of the tribe Who could tote up-on a ridge or gal-lop up a moun-tain side Who could haul a hun-ter's bur-den, turn a buf-fa-lo stam - pede. The horse that wore the spot-ted coat was born with match-less speed.

Chorus

Thun-der Roll - ing in the moun-tains Leads the peo-ple a - cross the great di- vide There's blood on the snow in the hills of I - da-ho But the heart of the Ap-pa - loo-sa ne-ver died.

From the land of shooting waters to the peaks of the Coeur d'Alenes
    Thimble berries in the forests—elk grazing on the plains,
The People of the Coyote made their camp along the streams
    Of the green Wallowa Valley when fences had no names.
And they bred a strain of horses, the treasure of the tribe
    Who could tote upon a ridge or gallup up a mountainside
Who could haul a hunter's burden, turn a buffalo stampede.
    The horse that wore the spotted coat was born with matchless speed.

CHORUS:
Thunder Rolling in the mountains
Leads the people across the great divide
There's blood on the snow in the hills of Idaho
But the heart of the Appaloosa never died.

In the winter came the crowned ones near frozen in the cold
    Bringing firearms and spyglass, and a book that saves the soul.
The people gave them welcome, nursed them 'til their strength returned
    And they studied the talking paper—its mysteries to learn.
In the shadow of the mission sprang up farms and squatter towns.
    The plain was lined with fences, the plow blade split the ground.
In the shallows of the Clearwater gold glittered in the pan
    And the word came down from Washington—remove the Indian!

The chief spoke to his people in his anger and his pain
    "I am no more Chief Joseph, 'Rolling Thunder' is my name.
They condemn us to a wasteland of barren soil and stone.
    We will fight them if we must—but we'll find another home."
They fled into the Bitterroot—an army at their heels.
    They fought at Whitebird Canyon, they fought at Misery Hill
'Til the colonel saw his strategy and sent the order down
    To kill the Appaloosa wherever it be found.

Twelve hundred miles retreating—three times over the divide
    A horse their only safety—their only ally.
Three thousand Appaloosa perished with the tribe.
    The people and their horses were dying side by side.
Thunder-Rolling-in-the-Mountains—"my heart is sick and sad.
    Our children now are freezing—the old chiefs are dead.
The hunger takes our spirit, the wounds are deep and sore.
    From where the sun now stands—I will fight no more."

They were sent to Oklahoma where malaria ran rife
    Still more died of broken hearts from the land that gave them life.
And the man once known as Joseph at death was heard to say:
    "We have given up our horses—now they have gone away!"
But sometimes without warning—from a dull domestic herd
    A spotted horse's spirit wondrous will emerge.
Strong it is and fearless—nimble on the hill.
    Listening for Thunder—the Appaloosa's living still.

❖ *This ballad is reprinted from Vardis Fisher's splen-did collection* Idaho Lore, *which he prepared for the Federal Writers Project of the Works Progress Admin-istration (WPA) in 1939. Fisher was the state director for the project in Idaho. The ballad was written about the Indian fight at Kamiah Springs, October 22, 1879.*

—R.S.

KAMIAH SPRINGS

As Cited in Fisher

'Twas the summer of 1879.
As a young man in my prime,
I drove my stock to Washington
Across the Oregon line.

We started from big Buttercreek,
My friend, Job Smith, an' I,
An' we found the stockman's paradise
Where the bunch-grass grew waist-high.

An' our hearts were light an' happy;
Till one October night
The Injuns swooped down on us,
An' we had that awful fight.

An Injun held me by the hair;
His knife was raised on high;
A shot rang out from Job Smith's gun,
An' an Injun fell to die.

Quick as a cat, I leaped for guns;
A pair of Colts had I.
The moon was shining brightly,
An' Indians fell close by.

Two score years have passed an' gone
Since that bright October night.
My friend, Job Smith, is sleeping now;
I live to tell the fight.

By now I'm old an' feeble,
an' my days are nearly o'er.
Job, have my cayuse saddled
When we meet on yon bright shore.

They may have their choo-choo wagons there;
Likewise, their aeroplanes,
But I'll take the deck of a cayuse,
An' ride the western range.

"Indian Dick's" lodge. Fort Hall, 1878. Shoshone. (Photo courtesy of the Smithsonian Institution)

❖*The recipes for chokeberry jelly, sage tea, and dried meat are from the* Sho-Ban News, *Fort Hall. Alta Guzman of the Nez Perce Tribe told me of the Indian butter.* —R.S.

Mrs. SoHappy, Kamiah. (Photo courtesy of Idaho State Historical Society)

CHOKECHERRY JELLY (Yield: five pounds jelly)
3 cups chokecherry juice
   3 1/2 pounds ripe cherries
6 1/2 cups sugar
1 bottle liquid pectin
1/4 tsp. almond extract (optional)

Stem the cherries. Add to 3 cups boiling water. Simmer, covered, for 15 minutes. Pit the cherries working over a bowl so you won't lose any juice. Squeeze cherries and juice through jelly bag or cheesecloth. Measure 3 cups of juice and add to sugar in large saucepan.

Mix well and add almond flavoring. Bring to boil over high heat, stirring constantly.

Add pectin. Bring to full rolling boil for one minute, stirring constantly. Remove from heat and skim off foam with metal spoon.

Pour into jelly glasses and cover at once with 1/8 inch hot paraffin.

Chokecherry tea is made from the inner bark and is used as a remedy for diarrhea.

SAGEBRUSH TEA
20 tender young sprigs of sagebrush, washed
2 quarts cold water

Place the sagebrush and water in large saucepan. Bring to a boil, cover, and simmer for 15 minutes. Turn heat off and let steep for 10 minutes. Strain and serve. Sweeten and add slice of lemon if desired.

"TA-O" or DRY MEAT
This is a real delicacy due to its scarcity. My grandfather, Reverend Stringfellow, used to make this meat. He basted it with wild blackberry juice as it was drying.

Slice venison into long strips 1/4 inch thick and sprinkle with salt. The strips are then hung over cedar or aspen poles which are stripped of their bark and suspended. Turn strips four or five times each day for two days. When fully dry, place in gunny sacks for winter storage. As needed, the strips are taken and placed in the oven to bake for several minutes, removed, and allowed to cool, then placed in a canvas sack and pounded with an iron rod and hammer until shredded and powdery.

INDIAN BUTTER
Crack some marrow bones and cover them with water in a large stock-pot . . . bring to a boil and cook until marrow rises to the top of the water . . . skim off marrow and force through a cheesecloth. Add shredded or powdered meat . . . spread on toast.

Stagecoach on Blue Lakes Grade. (Photo courtesy of Twin Falls Public Library)

WE'RE COMING IDAHO!

SETTLERS AND IMMIGRANTS

O! Wait, Idaho!
We're coming, Idaho;
Our four horse team
Will soon be seen
Way out in Idaho.

Doris Sammons
Challis, Idaho

A nd they did come.

They came to see the light. They came drawn like daytime moths by the morning light shining on the mountains. Idaho has always been a place to come to. Even the Native Americans came from somewhere else to get here. Idaho is a seemingly endless bounty, a place of adventure and challenge. People came to grab land and strike it rich. Some came to escape oppression and others to impose their will on the land—or on their neighbors. They brought their customs, stories, and songs. Their lore expresses the deep yearning for home and security given up in exchange for a new life in a new place. But their lore also expresses their fears and misconceptions about the people whom they met here.

Idaho's peoples and cultures are so varied it would be impossible to include examples from every immigrant group. So instead I have tried to present a sample of our human riches (which we have often treated so carelessly) and examine the confusion and energy which this collision of cultures continues to produce.

—R.S.

Doris Sammons brought this song to us at the Challis song swap. She got it from a neighbor, Mrs. Mary Pierson, who came from Colorado and who died in 1971 at the age of 97. I first heard this song in New York State when it was sung by the great singer, Frank Warner. This version was in a notebook that came from the late 1800's.

—R.S.

WE'RE COMING IDAHO

They say there is a land
where crys-tal wa-ters flow O'er beds of quartz and pur-est gold, Way out in I-da-ho.
Oh, wait, I-da-ho; We're com-ing I-da-ho, Our four horse team will soon be seen, Way out in I-da-ho. They

They say there is a land,
    Where crystal waters flow,
      O'er beds of quartz and purest gold,
    Way out in Idaho.

CHORUS:

O! Wait, Idaho!
    We're coming, Idaho;
    Our four "hoss" team
      Will soon be seen
Way out in Idaho.

We're bound to cross the plains,
    And up the mountains go,
      We're bound to see our fortunes there,
    Way out in Idaho.

We'll need no pick or spade,
No shovel, pan, or hoe,
    The largest chunks are top of ground,
Way out in Idaho.

We'll see hard times no more,
And want we'll never know,
    When once we've filled our sacks with gold,
Way out in Idaho.

❖❖❖

Most of the Chinese immigrants who came to Idaho entered this country via California. One of the more remarkable testimonies to the Chinese experience has been preserved at Angel Island in San Francisco Bay, the main entry point on the West Coast. Many of the Chinese immigrants wrote and carved their experiences into the posts, walls, and bed frames of the facility. The immigration center has been preserved in recognition of the harsh treatment the Chinese received. The poems cited here appeared in Island, Poetry and History of Chinese Immigrants on Angel Island 1910-1940, *edited by Mark Lai, Genny Lim and Judy Yung (San Francisco, 1986).*

—Robert McCarl

from ANGEL ISLAND

傷我華僑留木屋，

實因種界厄瀛臺。

摧殘尚說持人道，

應悔當初冒險來。

I am distressed that we Chinese are detained
    in this wood building.
It is actually racial barriers which cause
    difficulties on Yingtai Island.[1]

    Even while they are tyrannical, they still
    claim to be humanitarian.
I should regret my taking the risks of coming
    in the first place.

[1] *An island in the Nan Hai (Southern Lake), west of the Forbidden City in Peking. Emperor Guangxu (1875-1908) was imprisoned here by the Empress Dowager Cixi in 1898 after a coup d'etat to halt his reform programs.*

詳恨番奴不奉公，
頻施苛例逞英雄。
凌虐華僑兼背約，
百般專制驗勾蟲。
醫生苛待不堪言，
勾蟲刺血更心酸。
食了藥膏又食水，
猶如啞佬食黃連。

I thoroughly hate the barbarians because they
  do not respect justice.
They continually promulgate harsh laws to
  show off their prowess.
They oppress the overseas Chinese and also
  violate treaties.
They examine for hookworms[2] and practice
  hundreds of despotic acts.

I cannot bear to describe the harsh treatment
  by the doctors.
Being stabbed for blood samples and
  examined for hookworms[3] was even more
  pitiful.
After taking the medicine, I also drank
  liquid,[4]
Like a dumb person eating the huanglian.[5]

Unidentified miners at Royal Place, Rocky Bar region. Ca. 1900.
(Photo courtesy of Idaho State Historical Society)

[2] *Applicants for entry were examined for hookworm. Dur-*
ing the earlier years, infestation with the parasite was
cause for deportation. Later, patients were required to
undergo medical treatment before landing.
[3] *See note 2.*

[4] *Liquid medicine.*
[5] *"Coptis teeta," a bitter herb. "A dumb person eating the*
'huanglian'" is a victim who cannot voice his complaints
to anyone.

刻薄同胞實可憐，
醫生刺血最心酸。
冤情滿腹憑誰訴？
徘徊搔首問蒼天。

為口奔馳馳到監，
困愁愁食亦心煩。
薄待華人黃菜餐，
弱質難當實為難。

It is indeed pitiable the harsh treatment of
our fellow countrymen.
The doctor extracting blood caused us the
greatest anguish.
Our stomachs are full of grievances, but to
whom can we tell them?
We can but pace to and fro, scratch our
heads, and question the blue sky.

I hastened here for the sake of my stomach
and landed promptly in jail.
Imprisoned, I am melancholy; even when I
eat, my heart is troubled.
They treat us Chinese badly and feed us
yellowed greens.[6]
My weak physique cannot take it; I am truly
miserable.

[6] Salted cabbage.

Wedding group in 1906. (Photo courtesy of Idaho State Historical
Society)

❖*Vern Tregaskis was a policeman back when we had a Chinatown in Boise. I still remember the basalt and iron buildings that housed the herbalist, the bankers, and the most tantalizing and exotic members of our community. I also remember that if you knew enough to ask for the right things, you could get a real Chinese meal at the Bamboo Gardens, instead of chow mein and pork and seeds.*

I remember being so curious about the Chinese—curious about how they got here and curious about who they were. I had so many questions no one could (or would) answer. And when I was old enough and smart enough to find out for myself, I learned that the answer was one I did not want to know. The Chinese were so miserably treated here in Idaho that the kindest story I can find about their sojourn in this unforgiving country is that a young policeman named Vern Tregaskis used to sneak opium to a jailed Chinese gentleman so that he would not suffer the horrors of withdrawal in jail. Yet having told that story, I realize that it favors the white policeman and reinforces yet another negative stereotype about the Chinese. This is a touchy subject, but an important one that keeps me mindful of the negative aspect of our traditions and folklore.

At one time, of course, nearly 700 Chinese (mostly

Chinese New Year, 1905. (Photo courtesy of Idaho State Historical Society)

men) lived and worked in the Owyhee Mountains in Idaho. They were unassuming and law-abiding citizens who played a crucial part in the development of the region through their labor, not to mention the special taxes they paid. Scholars, such as Li-hua Yu who helped me locate the Angel Island poems, are only now recognizing the important contribution made by the Chinese to the economic development of Idaho. Mac Parkins, organizer and first president of the Owyhee County Historical Society, illustrates other contributions made by the Chinese in the following poem. This piece is one of a series of poems he wrote about the Owyhee mines. —R.S.

THE TRANSPLANTS
by Mac Parkins

Take any man, from any land—
Transplant him in his adult days
To some strange, distant, countryside—
Then see who has the strangest ways!

This never fails to slight the few;
Fate gives deciding to the most!
Suspicion weaves an early web,
And Fairness seldom plays the host!

But men are men in all respects,
And deepest needs are all the same.
When surface shows some minor change,
Environment should take the blame!

Ambition, plus a naked need
For self-preserving limb and life,
Brought Chinese workers to the mines;
Sometimes exchanging strife—for strife!

They found a place, and filled a need;
(Though bigotry ordained it low.)
With resignation centuries old,
They lived to work—and proved it so!

These helped to make the districts hum—
And shared developmental pride—
These set a law-abiding pace—
And took injustice in their stride!

These gave their lives in heavy toil;
And took but little in return.
These brought a color to these towns;
These brought a truth that all should learn;

Take any man, from any land—
Transplant him in his adult days
To some strange, distant, countryside—
They'll say he has the strangest ways!

❖ *Barre Toelken, a Professor of Folklore at Utah State University, tells us that this song came from an old retired logger by the name of Henry Tams in Moscow, Idaho. "The story is one that I've heard in various parts of Idaho," Barre says, "and also in Washington. Somebody will point out the local cemetery and tell you that the Chinese were buried along one side with the bandits, desperados, Catholics, and so on. They will also tell you that one Chinese guy was hung by mistake and that the local people tried to make up for it by putting an epitaph on his grave that said, 'Hanged by mistake.' I've had people tell me this actually happened in Florence, Idaho, and a couple of other places. I've never been able to find any historical background for it, but the image also comes up in the California gold fields. So, if the song is at all realistic, it is mostly real because it indicates the attitude toward Chinese miners. This is a song by those who see the Chinese as expendable. In it, we also see the idea of the uneducated frontier judge becoming famous because he hands down judgments that benefit the community."*

—R.S.

OLD JUDGE DUFFY

As Sung by Barre Toelken *Traditional*

Old John Martin Duffy was judge in a court in a small mining town in the west although he knew nothin' about rules of the law, For judge he was one of the best. One night in the winter a murder occurred, And our blacksmith accused of the crime. We caught him red-handed and though he'd two trials, but the verdict was guilty each time. Now he was the only good blacksmith we had and we wanted to spare him his life. So Duffy rose up in the court like a lord and with these words he settled the strife. "I move we discharge him. We need him in town," And he

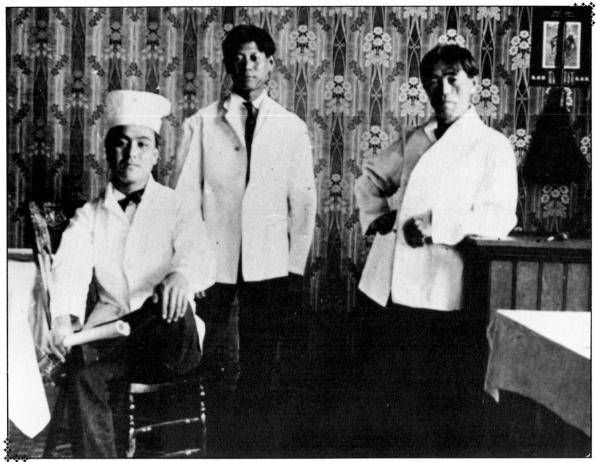

Chinese restaurant staff.(Photo courtesy of Idaho State Historical Society)

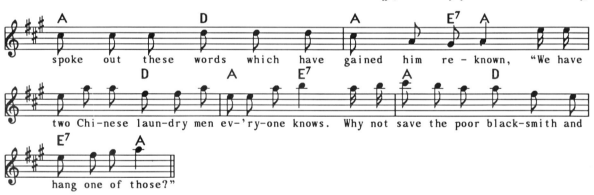

spoke out these words which have gained him re - known, "We have

two Chi-nese laun-dry men ev-'ry-one knows. Why not save the poor black-smith and

hang one of those?"

Old John Martin Duffy was judge in a court,
    In a small mining town in the west;
Although he knew nothing 'bout rules of the law,
    For Judge he was one of the best.

One night in the winter a murder occurred,
    And our blacksmith accused of the crime.
We caught him red-handed and though he'd two
    trials,
    But the verdict was guilty each time.

Now he was the only good blacksmith we had,
    And we wanted to spare him his life,
So Duffy rose up in the court like a lord,
    And with these words he settled the strife.

"I move we dismiss him; We need him in town,"
    And he spoke out the words that have gained
    him renown,
"We have two Chinese laundrymen, everyone
    knows;
    Why not save the poor blacksmith and hang one
    of those?"

I was a very young twenty-three-year-old new mother living about as far away from my family in Idaho as I could get. I loved being the only American family in a wonderful Japanese town, but I was also feeling the distance from things familiar. My mother had come over for the birth of my son, but then returned home.

My friend Tetsuko Koke (The-One-Who-Would-Be-My-Maid-But-Thank-Goodness-Became-My-Friend-Instead) understood my loneliness; she offered to teach me some songs for the "made in Japan" baby. And so I learned "Ame, Ame," the

child's song about the rain, and sang it to the delight of my new son.

Almost 25 years later, I was visiting a young couple in Pocatello who had just welcomed their first child. The mother was Japanese, and the oba'sama, grandmother, had come from Japan to be there for her grandchild's arrival. She spoke no English, and was feeling isolated from the culture around her. She held her granddaughter, smiled softly, and began to sing, "Ame Ame."

—Mary Alice Shaw
Pocatello

JAPANESE RAIN SONG

As Sung by Mary-Alice Shaw　　　　　　*Traditional*

Á-me, Á-me, fú-re, fú-ra Ka-san-ga Ja-no-me-de-o-mu-ka-i

U-re-shi-na Pi-chi, pi-chi, cha-pu, cha-pu lan dan dan

Pi-chi, pi-chi, cha-pu, cha-pu lan, dan dan.

Bert's Corner Cup. (Photo courtesy of Michael Cordell)

Áme, áme, fúre, fúra
　Kasan-ga
Janome-de-omukai
　Ureshina
　CHORUS:
Pichi, pichi, chapu, chapu
　Lan dan dan
Pichi, pichi, chapu, chapu
　Lan, dan, dan
Ára, ára ano ko-wa
　Zubunu-re-da
Yanagi-no-koaréte
　Naiteru

　CHORUS:

Mary Alice Shaw lives in Pocatello, Idaho, and surrounds herself with people, plants, and animals. She takes part in life with an energy that seems inexhaustible, and her recollection of learning the "Japanese Rain Song" is as graceful as her singing of it was at U.S. Bert's Corner Cup. (Photo courtesy of Michael Cordell)

❖ *This song and other versions of it were sung as nonsense songs. We got this first version from June Marshall, a friend in American Falls; "The Chineeman" is from Virginia DeFoggi (Pocatello), who* *learned it from her grandmother, Mary Smith Christiansen (born in Hiram, Utah). Both versions exemplify White perceptions about the Chinese in the early part of this century.* —R.S.

THE CHINEEMAN

As Sung by Virginia DeFoggi

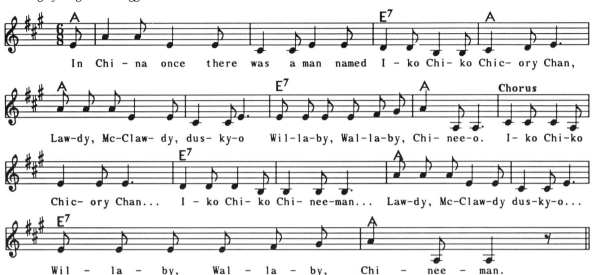

In Chi-na once there was a man named I-ko Chi-ko Chic-ory Chan, Law-dy, Mc-Claw-dy, dus-ky-o Wil-la-by, Wal-la-by, Chi-nee-o. I-ko Chi-ko Chic-ory Chan... I-ko Chi-ko Chi-nee-man... Law-dy, Mc-Claw-dy dus-ky-o... Wil-la-by, Wal-la-by, Chi-nee-man.

THE CHINAMAN

This Chinaman was a very fine man
His name was Chig-a ree-Chian
His legs were short, his feet were tall
This Chinaman could not walk at all.
CHORUS:
Chig-a rig, a rye a ray
A diddle de de ka mop pe may
A toola ma tisk a tangee oh
a gallopin wallopin chineo.

This Chinaman was a very fine man
He washed his face in a frying pan
He combed his hair with a wagon wheel and
died from a toothache in his heel.
CHORUS:
One day this Chinaman did die,
And in his coffin he did lie . . .
They shipped him over to Japan
And that was the end of the Chinaman.

THE CHINEEMAN

In China once there was a man
    Named Iko Chiko Chicory Chan,
Lawdy, McClawdy, dusky-o
    Willaby, wallaby, Chinee-o.

One day the people of the town
    Went up the hill to roll him down . . .
From top to bottom they all began
    To chuckle and play with the Chinee-man.
CHORUS:
Iko Chiko Chicory Chan . . .
    Iko Chiko, Chineeman . . .
Lawdy, McClawdy, dusky-o . . .
    Willaby, wallaby, Chinee-o.

One day the Chineeman did die,
    And in his coffin he did lie . . .
They shipped him over to Japan,
    And that was the end of the Chineeman.

I would guess "Off to Boise City" was a song sung by Blacks when they heard about the Emancipation Proclamation—or maybe the winning of the Civil War. I believe it was sung by Blacks working in the silver and gold mines of central Idaho.

In the last verse, "The elephant ate his potpie and danced with Mr. Crocodile" unlikely images appear—

maybe as unlikely as they thought the Emancipation Proclamation was. I have had a couple of people suggest that those might have been political references of the day. The song may be based on a minstrel show from back east in the mid-1800's, but its local application is pretty specific. —Barre Toelken

I'M OFF TO BOISE CITY

As Sung by Barre Toelken   *Traditional*

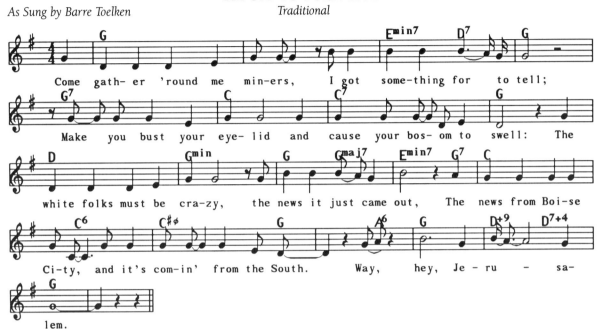

Come gather 'round me miners, I got something for to tell;
Make you bust your eyelid and cause your bosom to swell:
The white folks must be crazy, the news it just came out,
The news from Boise City, and it's comin' from the South.
Way, hey, Jerusalem.

I have a wooden shovel, and another made of tin,
And the way I scoop that gravel up, it surely is a sin.
If them city white folks ask us who we be,
Just tell'em it's the California Gold Mining Company.
Way, hey, Jerusalem.

I'm goin' downtown, the telegraph to hire,
And see if they need a colored man to greasen up the wire.
When I get down to Bannock, I'll take a cargo train,
Then on over to Centerville and I'll telegraph again.
Way, hey, Jerusalem.

Old Dan Tucker needn't want for his supper any more,
'Cause Abe's gonna take him down to that Old Virginia shore.
I said, "So long and goodbye, my little Mary Blummer,
I'm off to Boise City, but I'll come back to get ya."
Way, hey, Jerusalem.

The elephant ate his pot pie and danced with the crocodile,
Oh, Jerusalem, where I was bound to go.
Was off to Boise City with a shovel and a hoe,
Pack up all your shiny clothes and we'll be on the go.
Way, hey, Jerusalem.

Black fiddler.
(Photo courtesy of
Idaho State
Historical Society)

Boise, Idaho, views, Charles L. Ostner Lithograph, 1878. (Photo
courtesy of Idaho State Historical Society)

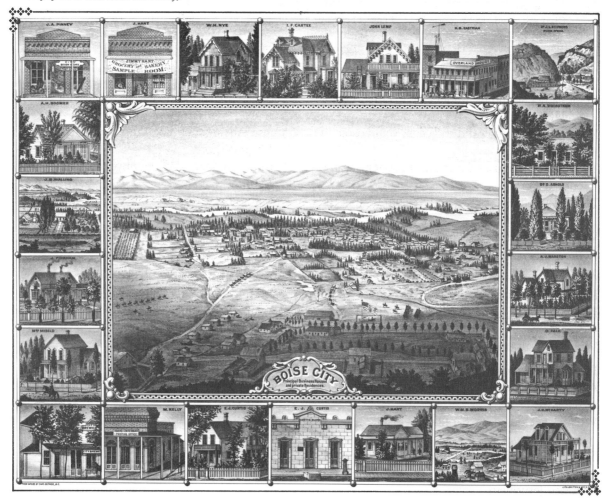

James Sangroniz, a member of the Oinkari dancers, was kind enough to sing me "Amerikaterá Joan Nintzan," which I first heard from Father Santos Recalde years ago. I remember James' uncle, Joe Sangroniz, playing the bones and singing old ballads at the Basque Center when I was in high school. His playing and singing made me feel like I'd gone backwards centuries, to another time and place. Many young Basques are working hard to preserve this link to the tap-root of their tree of life. (Photo courtesy of Michael Cordell)

❖ *Outside of the Basque country in Spain and France, Idaho has the largest population of Basques in the world. The Basque people who live here are dedicated to keeping alive their songs, music, and traditions by teaching them to their children.*

I first heard the following song, as well as many others, from Father Santos Recalde. He sang some additional verses, which told of a young man going to America because his sweetheart wouldn't marry him since he didn't have enough money. And then, the young man returns with lots of money but also the news that he is carving a cradle for his second child! The message, of course, is to accept the good man and don't look for his money.

The version of the song below is from Mary Carmen Totorica, who says, "I learned 'Ameriketara Joan Nintzan' here in Boise. In Guernica, Spain I never heard songs in Basque—it was not allowed because of Franco. In school, on the radio, everything was in Spanish. Now, I have learned the Basque songs and I teach them to the little children." —R.S.

AMERIKETARÁ JOAN NINTZAN

As Sung by Mary Carmen Totorica   *Traditional*

A-me-ri-ke-ta-ra joan nin-tzan xen-ti-mo-rik ga-be, An-dik e-tor-ri nin-tzan mai-ti-a bost mi-lloi-en ja-be; Txin txin, txin txin, di-ru-a-ren ots-a A-re-xek e-ma-ten dit mai-ti-a bi-o-tzi-an po-za.

AMERIKETARÁ JOAN NINTZAN
Ameriketará joan nintzan
    xentimorik gabe
Andik etorri nintzan, maitia
    bost milloien jabe.
Txin txin, txin txin,
    diruaren otsa,
Arexek ematen dit, maitia
    biotzian poza.

I WENT TO AMERICA
I went to America
    without owning a cent
From there I returned, my dear,
    owning five million.
Chin, chin, chin, chin (onomatopoeia)
    the noise of money —
That gives, my dear,
    happiness to my heart.

❖ *This song was a favorite of Domingo Ansotegui, who played the tambourine with Jimmy Jausoro— Idaho's best known Basque musician and National Heritage Award winner. The young singers think of it* *as a tribute to him. It urges the Basque children to learn the songs and dances and keep the Basque music alive.*
—R.S.

AURRAK IKAS-AZUE

As Sung by James Sangroniz Traditional

Aur-rak i-kas za-zu-e es-kua-raz min-tza-tzen, On-gi pi-lo-tan e-ta

on-es-ki dan-tza-tzen. Aur-rak i-kas za-zu-e es-kua-raz min-tza-tzen, On-gi pi

lo-tan e-ta on-es-ki dan-tza-tzen. Ai-re tun txi-ki-tun ai-re tun la-i-re

Ai-re tun txi-ki-tun ai-re tun la-i-re Ai-re tun txi-ki-tun ai-re

tun la-i-re Ai-re tun txi-ki-tun lai-re tun lai-re O-le!

Aurrak ikas-zue eskuaraz mintzatzen,
Ongi pilotan eta oneski dantzatzen . . . (bis)
 Aire tun txikitun aire tun laire
 Aire tun txikitun aire tun laire
 Aire tun txikitun aire tun laire
 Aire tun txikitun aire tun laire . . . O le!

Gure kantu xaarrak konserba ditzagun
Aire pollitagorik ez da sortu neun . . . (bis)

Ez aantz bein ere sort-erri ederra,
Aren mendiak eta itsaso bazterra . . . (bis)

Biotz leiala ere atxik aitameri
Eta nunbait goait dagon gazte maiteari . . . (bis)

❖ *I first learned the song from Father Recalde. This more complete version below came from Mary Carmen Totorica. Although the English translation is very rough and incomplete, I want to thank Marie Aburasturi for her assistance with it.* —R.S.

BELENGO PORTALIAN

As Sung by Mary Carmen Totorica   *Traditional*

Basque picnic, Boise, 1933. (Photo courtesy of Idaho State Historical Society)

BELENGO PORTALIAN	BETHLEHEM STABLE
Mesias zarritan aginduzana	Often among the angels
Aingeru artian dator gugana	He came to us.
Gloria zeruan	Glory in the heavens.
Gloria lurrian	Glory on earth.
an aingeruak	There are angels
dagos Belenen	in Bethlehem.
Belengo portalian	In a stable in Bethlehem
Negu gogorrian	in the hard winter
Jayada gure Jesus	our baby Jesus was born
Askatzo batian	in a manger.
Estarki barik dado	He is naked.
da bere artian	He is among us.
Gustis santua dana	He is all-holy.
Zeru ta lurrian	In heaven and on earth.
Antzen dago la . . .	He is there . . . yes.
Gure Jesus la . . .	The small lamb is there.
Antzen dago . . . bay	His mother tells him to sleep
Aurtzo tzikia antzen dago	but with his eyes
Amak ezantzo lo egiteko	The baby lamb tells her,
Bano artzoak	"Mother, I can't."
Begiakin ezantendio	la ra la ra . . .
Ama ezim	
la ra la ra . . .	

45

Mary Carmen Totorica came to us from Guernica. She sang me many Basque songs. I went to a teaching session at the Basque Center and watched this tireless, beautiful woman singing and dancing with forty more children all singing, "Aurrak": "Children, you should learn your language . . ." This is a lesson we all could use and enjoy. (Photo courtesy of Michael Cordell)

RECIPES

HEAVY FRIED CREAM

5 cups raw milk
1/8 tsp. salt
1 cup flour
a piece of cinnamon
5 tbsps. sugar
a piece of lemon peel
1 egg yolk and 1 egg

Into a large pot, put 4 of the 5 cups of milk, salt, lemon peel and cinnamon stick (these should be small pieces). Warm on medium high heat. In a bowl put the other cup of milk and the egg yolk and blend well. Sift the sugar and flour together and add to the milk and egg yolk mixture. Now add the warmed mixture and the latter mixture together. Put back on heat and stir constantly — it should boil for five minutes. Remove from heat and pour onto large flat plates to cool for three or more hours — until the mixture is cool. Cut into squares about 2 inches. Put out some flour in a plate, dip the squares in this to coat lightly. Beat the egg and put the squares through the beaten egg. Heat 6 tbsps. of lard and 6 tbsps. of oil in a large frying pan. When the grease is hot put the squares into the pan and fry until both sides are lightly browned. Just before serving sprinkle the tops of the squares with sugar and cinnamon. Serve while warm.

This is a very old Basque dessert which is especially liked during the long winter months.
— Mrs. M. Carmen Totorica, Boise

MARADI ETA ARDAU:
PEARS IN WINE

Boil enough Sherry wine with 1 teaspoon of cinnamon and a bit of cloves to cover pears. Let the pears stand in the wine until ready to serve.
— Mrs. Jim Jausoro, Boise

GAZPATXO: BASQUE FISH DISH

1/2 medium size onion — chopped
2 fairly good sized potatoes — cut in small squares
1 green pepper — cut in small pieces
3 spoonfuls of tomatoes
1/2 pound of tuna or bonito (preferably fresh) in chunks
salt to taste, dash of pepper, hot if preferred, or sweet
3 cups of water
2 slices of bread cut into squares (small) and fried in oil

Place enough oil in cooking dish or casserole to cover bottom; add onions and brown. Add potatoes, tomatoes, green peppers — add chunks of tuna — add three cups of water. Bring the mixture to boil and cut the fire to slow; cook for several hours. Cut the bread into small squares and deep fry until brown and put on top when it is ready to be served. This will serve good portions for four people, and may be served with a salad as main dish.

— Mrs. Espe Alegria, Boise

❖ *Mrs. Alegria has served as Mistress of Ceremonies for a Basque radio program in the area. She has been an ardent worker for the preservation of Basque history within the state of Idaho.* — R.S.

MAKALAU ETA PIPERS:
CODFISH AND PEPPERS

Soak 1 pound of codfish overnight. Rinse with fresh water and pat dry. Cut fish into individual serving pieces. Roll in flour first, then egg and fry in oil with a clove of garlic. Place in a flat pan. Simmer 1 medium size can of pimento in oil with garlic. Pour over the fish and bake at 350 degrees for 30 minutes. Serves 8.

— Mrs. Jim Jausoro, Boise

Matilda Machacek organized the first concert of our Centennial Project for us at the senior center in Buhl. There is a genuine Czech community there, one that came together to give us the gifts of good company, songs, dancing, and a spread of homemade pastries — a nourishing beginning for our journey through this multi-faceted young state.   (Photo courtesy of Michael Cordell)

TA NAŠE PÍSNIČKA ČESKÁ

As Sung by Matilda Machacek   *Traditional*

Ty naše písničky	Our pretty Czech songs
jsou jak ty perličky	Are like those precious pearls
na sňůrce navleče.	Lovingly strung on a string.
Tolik je krásy vnich	There's much beauty in them
a je to velký hřích,	And it's a great sin
Že jsou tak utlače né.	They should be so oppressed.
Ta naše písnička česká,	This is our beautiful Czech song
Ta je tak hezká, tak hezká,	So lovely, so lovely begun
Tak jako nalouce kytička,	Just like a flower in the meadow
Vyrostla ta naše písnička.	Grew our beautiful song you know.
Až se ta písničk a ztratí	If ever our song becomes lost
Pak už nic nebudem mít,	Then nothing else will remain.
Jestli nám zahyne, všecko	Should it once perish,
s ní pomine,	All else with it will vanish
Potom už nebudem žít.	Even we no more then will live.

49

KDE DOMOV MŮJ?

As Sung by Matilda Machacek   Traditional

Kde do- mov můj? Kde do- mov můj? Vo-ca hu — čí po lu-

či - nách, Bo- ry šu — mí po ska-li- nách, V sa dest kví se zja ra květ, Zem-ský

ráj to na po- hled! A to jest ta krá - sná ze - mě Ze-mě

čes - ká do- mov můj! Ze- mě čes - ká do- mov můj!

KDE DOMOV MŮJ?	WHERE IS MY HOME?
Kde domov můj? Kde domov můj?	Where is my home? Where is my home?
Voda hučí po lučinách,	Streams are rushing through thy meadows,
Bory šumí po skalinách,	Rocks, where fragrant pine grows,
V sadě skvi se z jara květ,	The parks in bloom in such array
Zemský raj to na pohled!	An earthly paradise portray!
A to jest ta krásná země,	Is that land of wondrous beauty,
Země česká, domov můj!	Is that Czech-land Homeland mine!
Země česká, domov můj!	Is that Czech-land Homeland mine!

Norwegian dancers. (Photo courtesy of Idaho State Historical Society)

KOLAĆE

2 pkgs. yeast
1 1/2 cups boiled riced potatoes
8 cups flour
2/3 cup sugar
1 rounded tbsp. salt
2 cups milk
3 well beaten eggs (optional - may add 2 to 4 drops yellow food coloring)
Lemon rind

Into a 2-cup measuring cup or bowl, put 1/4 cup lukewarm water, 1 tsp. sugar and add 2 pkgs. yeast, stir and let rise while preparing boiled riced potatoes. Heat milk to lukewarm, add beaten eggs and lemon rind. Into large bowl sift flour, sugar, salt.

Into large mixer bowl put shortening, riced potatoes and beat until smooth. Add milk mixture, yeast and about half of flour, continue beating at low speed (4 or 5) until smooth. Change beaters to kneaders. Add rest of flour slowly, scraping sides as mixer needs dough. Takes about 5-7 minutes. If you do not have dough kneaders, beat with wooden spoon until dough is silky and smooth. Turn into a large well-greased pan or grease the pan in which you've mixed dough. Let rise till double in bulk (about 1 1/2 hour). During that time prepare and grease well baking pans, a cup of melted shortening with pastry brush. When dough has risen, form into balls about size of pheasant egg (about 1 1/4 in. in diameter). Place on greased pan about 1" apart and brush with grease. Let rise about 20-30 minutes or until double in size. Brush between rolls again with grease. Make depressions in center and fill with your favorite fruit, cottage cheese, or poppy seed filling. Sprinkle fruit filled with streusel or coconut; let rise again for about 10 minutes and bake at 425 degrees for 12-15 minutes or until done. Remove from oven. Brush *Kolaće* with melted oleo or butter. Yield 5 to 6 dozen *Kolaće*.

After poppy seed *Kolaće* have cooled, sprinkle with powdered sugar. On top of cottage cheese, a blanched almond may be placed in center before baking.

Approx. cost $2.50

—Matilda Machacek

The same basic dough is used for donuts and *rohliky*. Yields 50-60 donuts; 4-5 dozen *rohliky* or crescent rolls.

EXTRA NOTE: Two egg whites not used in cottage cheese filling may be beaten with a little water and sugar and brushed on Kolaće around filling before baking. This will give a glazed, rosy brown color to the finished baked product. If no egg white on hand, a whole egg beaten and added with 1 or 2 tbsp. milk and a little sugar may be used with the same effect.

—Matilda Machacek

PRUNE FILLING FOR KOLACE

1 lb. dried prunes. Cover with water and cook until soft. Drain off liquid and save. Cool. Remove seeds and put thru' grinder, add 2 tbsp. butter (optional), 1/2 cup sugar (more may be added if sweeter taste desired), 1/8 tsp. cloves, 1 tsp. cinnamon, 1 tsp. lemon rind and mix well. If too thick add juice to right consistency (like jam).

Approx. cost $1.40

—Matilda Machacek

POPPY SEED FILLING FOR KOLAĆE

1 cup ground poppy seed
1/3 cup melted butter
1/2 cup canned milk or cream
1 1/2 tbsp. lemon juice
1/2 tsp. cinnamon
1/2 cup sugar or sweeten to taste

Blend all above ingredients and simmer for five minutes, stirring continually; will scorch easily, so keep heat low and stir. Add 1 cup dark raisins, cool. If too thick, add a little cream or canned milk at a time until right consistency.

After *Kolaće* are baked a little powdered sugar may be sprinkled over the poppy seed filling.

Approx. cost $1.50

—Matilda Machacek

Kolace and pastries. (Photo courtesy of Michael Cordell)

❖ *I do not know if it is because I have Irish blood in my veins, or if I just find Irish music entertaining and seductive, but everywhere we went throughout the state we heard Irish tunes and songs. From Bonners Ferry in the north to Lava Hot Springs in the south, we heard Idahoans of Irish descent celebrate their heritage. Beyond the ethnic stereotypes associated with the Irish (from the "gift of gab" to green beer) I have tried to include material in this section that recognizes the important contribution the Irish made to our state.*

This song came from Alma Schooler (Buhl), who learned it when she was about ten years old from a neighbor who sang it as the family sat working around the quilting frame. Alma dedicated this song in loving memory to Mrs. Gonterman. Unfortunately, we were not able to locate the music for this song. —R.S.

AN IRISH GIRL'S LAMENT

When leaving dear old Ireland; in the merry
    month of June
The birds were sweetly singing and all nature
    seemed in tune.
An Irish girl accosted me with a sad tear in her eye
And with every word she spoke to me she bitterly
    did cry.
"Kind sir, I'd ask a favor. Oh, grant it to me please.
'Tis not much that I ask of you but will set my heart
    at ease.
Take these to my brother, for I have no other
And these are the shamrocks from his dear, old
    mother's grave.
Tell him since he went away how bitter was our lot.
The landlord came one winter's day and turned us
    from our plot.
Our troubles were so many, our friends so very few
And brother, dear, they're all I have and them I send
    to you."
Three leaves of shamrock, the Irishmen's sham-
    rock
From his own darling sister, the blessings to me she
    gave.
"Take them to my brother for I have no other
And these are the shamrocks from his dear old
    mother's grave."

Bud, Allan and Arthur Lambson.(Photo courtesy of Idaho State Historical Society)

❖ *I wrote this song in honor of my grandmothers' gardens. Everyone in my family had some Irish heritage, and this is my sentimental, Irish-American celebration of the flower with the green blossom I* *always thought was magic. Shaped like a small horn, clustered on a stalk, the flower is the color of spring. It looks as if you put your lips to it, you could play a tune for the green heart of an Irish fool.* —R.S.

THE BELLS OF IRELAND

As Sung by Rosalie Sorrels · Written by Rosalie Sorrels

These are the bells of Ire - land, that in my gar-den grow. My great-grand-mo-ther brought those seeds from Ire-land long a - go. Their mu-sic it is wild and sad, like or-phaned an-gels sing and you must lis-ten in your soul to hear the bells of Ire-land ring_____. My mo-ther's fa-ther had the look of Ire-land's he-roes bold, strong broad shoul-ders ra-ven eyes to look in-to your soul_____. My fa-ther's mo-ther's face was a map of the roads Maeve's feet had trod. "Rose of the world," I'm named for her— Lord, I love her lost old sod and these are the bells of Ire - land that in my gar-den grow. My great-grand mo-ther brought those seeds from Ire-land long a - go. Their mu-sic it is wild and sad, like or-phaned an-gels sing, and you must lis-ten in your soul to

hear the bells of Ire-land ring_____. I've ne-ver been to Ire-land

Tho' I sing of the cool green shore and I dream I must have lived

there some cen-tu-ry be-fore. I weep for the blood and the

trou-bles and I tend my gar-den well. Let the sweet green bells of

Ire - land out - ring the bells of hell. And these are the bells of Ire -

land that in my gar-den grow. My great-grand-mo-ther brought those seeds from

Ire-land long a - go. Their mu-sic it is wild and sad, like or-phaned an-gels

sing and you must lis-ten in your soul to hear the bells of Ire- land

ring _____.

CHORUS:
These are the bells of Ireland
  That in my garden grow . . .
My great-grandmother brought those seeds
  From Ireland long ago.
Their music, it is wild and sad,
  Like orphaned angels sing . . .
And you must listen in your soul to hear
  The bells of Ireland ring.

My mother's father had the look
  Of Ireland's heroes bold . . .
Strong, broad shoulders . . . raven eyes,
  To look into your soul.
My father's mother's face was a map
  Of the roads Maeve's feet had trod . . .
"Rose of the world" . . . I'm named for her . .
  Lord, I love her lost old sod.

CHORUS:
I've never been to Ireland,
  Though I sing of the cool green shores . . .
And I dream I must have lived there
  Some century before.
I weep for the blood and the troubles
  And I tend my garden well . . .
Let the sweet green bells of Ireland
  Outring the bells of hell.
      CHORUS:
And these are the bells . . .

❖ We collected this song from Gary Oberbilling, who learned it from Frank N. Sprague of Fruitland, Idaho, in 1953. Mr. Sprague learned it from a cousin, Ford Wanamaker, in Nebraska around 1915. In his description of the song, Gary writes, "Frank Sprague had strong populist views. He came to Idaho by way of Nebraska and Colorado. He was my first guitar teacher. When I knew him, he was in his eighties and was usually an enthusiastic performer at the Old Time Fiddlers Festival in Weiser. His family is very musical as well. His daughter, Betty (Mrs. Joseph Hopper), is a fiddler as are his granddaughters, one of whom, Jana Jae, has performed on national television. Part of the humor of the songs lies in the bemused query, 'I'm a nice guy—how did I get into these things?' The 6/8 time and Irish references in the song might indicate that it comes from that tradition, although it may be a music hall song that was written to sound 'Irish.'"

—R.S.

HOW PLEASANT THAT WOULD BE

As Sung by Gary Oberbilling *Traditional*

Old P. T. Bar-num's Great Big Show is in an aw-ful stew.___ They've
lost their cur-i-o-si-ty and don't know what to do. It hap-pened just a
week a-go and how they wept and cried.___ When through the town the
news it spread that the big bab-boon had died. And they want-ed me to
take his place and do the best I could——to be locked up in a
great big cage, with mon-keys bad and good. They'd call me Crow-ley Num-ber Two; the
kids stick pins in me.___ They'd feed me can-dy and pea-nuts, Oh how
plea-sant that would be.

Old P. T. Barnum's great big show is in an awful stew—
They've lost their "curiosity," and don't know what to do.
It happened just a week ago, and how they wept and cried—
When through the town the news it spread that the big baboon had died.
And they wanted me to take his place, and do the best I could—
To be locked up in a great big cage, with monkeys bad and good.
They'd call me Crowley Number Two; the kids stick pins in me—
They'd feed me candy and peanuts—Oh how pleasant that would be!

McCarty and McLusky, too, had matched their dogs to fight—
They posted fifty dollars for to fight on Friday night.
We all went down to Cody's Place, McCarty's dog was there—
But we could not find McLusky, or his bull pup anywhere.
And they wanted me to take his place, and do the best I could—
"Go in the ring and fight him fair! We *know* your pluck is good."
They wanted me to strip my coat, and fight that dog you see—
He would tear my eyes, my nose, my ears—How pleasant that would be!

My sister had a policy upon her husband's life.
He ran away and left her broke; a disappointed wife.
She said: "If he was only dead, the insurance I could claim."
And so she bought a coffin, and on it had engraved his name.
And she wanted me to take his place, and do the best I could—
To play off dead and be locked up in a coffin made of wood.
And when the mourners had all gone, she *said* she'd set me free—
Perhaps she might forget it—Oh how pleasant that would be!

In Idaho, we sometimes tell outsiders that our state has three capitol cities: Spokane in the north, Boise in the center; and Salt Lake City in the south. As a hub, Salt Lake City still controls the great Mormon wheel just as it did in those early days after the Saints had completed their great western migration. The Mormon saga of the trek across the midwestern plains through the high Rocky Mountains to the once magnificent valley of the Great Salt Lake continues to be told and sung. Unlike many other groups who migrated West— especially those looking to make quick fortunes or those whose "work" took them temporarily away from their eastern homes—the Mormons came West intending to stay. Once they arrived in their promised land, Brigham Young instructed his people to make the desert bloom like a rose. And to some extent, the Mormons have done just that. I don't know of a more closely-knit or more hardworking people than the Mormons. Their symbol is the beehive—and Mormon culture continues to produce an abundance of story and song.

This traditional lyric, "The Lonesome Roving Wolves," for example, documents the difficult continental crossing the early Mormons made to Utah in the mid-1800's.

—Robert McCarl

THE LONESOME ROVING WOLVES

As Sung by Rosalie Sorrels   *Traditional*

The Mormons were camped down by the green grove
Where the clear waters flow from the mountains above. The wind it approached, all chilly and cold And we listened to the howling of those lonesome roving wolves.

The Mormons were camped down by the green grove,
Where the clear waters flow from the mountains above . . .
The wind it approached, all chilly and cold,
And we listened to the howling of the lonesome roving wolves.

The groans of the dying were heard in our camp,
And the cold chilly frost it was seen on our tent . . .
And the fear in our hearts can never be told,
As we listened to the howling of the lonesome roving wolves.

The grave of the stranger we left on the plain,
Down by the green grove, there forever to remain . . .
To remember his grave, we left ashes and coals
To hide him from the savages and the lonesome roving wolves.

But early next morning, just at the break of day
The drums and the fifes did play a reveille.
Our mules were brought in, our baggage for to pull . . .
And now we'll bid adieu to the lonesome roving wolves.

❖ *The text of this song came from William H. Avery (Blackfoot) and was first collected by Thomas Edward Cheney. It reflects the hostility toward enemies of the church that loyalists to the cause commonly felt.*

—R.S.

IN DEFENSE OF POLYGAMY

Written by William H. Avery

There is a bunch of whiskey bloats polluting our fair land;
They are here to see our country laws enforced;
They say that the laws, there ain't enough to punish Mormon crime,
And for more, they are always on the yelp.

CHORUS:
Murry holds the reins, the whip belongs to Zane,
Ole Ireland and his aid will go below;
And old Dixon will do well to engage a case in Hell,
For the road he is on will take him there, I know.

They say that if the Mormons will polygamy deny,
Like themselves take to houses of ill fame.
They will call them friends and brethren and will take them by the hand;
But in this, I think, they'll find they are lame.

They say that the Mormons are a set of low-down dragons,
And they're going to rid the land of such a crew,
Or they will build pens large enough to hold Mormon men,
And in them they will shove the women, too.

But the Mormons do not fear their threats and always will be found
To their God and to their constitution true;
They will support Columbus' cause and defend Columbus' laws;
Then with righteousness this nation will be blessed.

❖ *In their fascinating survey of Mormon Lore, Saints of Sage and Saddle (1956), Austin and Alta Fife write: "The legends which have helped to weld Mormonia into the homogeneous body and a respected institution have had their counterpart in an anti-Mormon lore of amazing vitality. Anti-Mormonism never was a positive, unified force, but rather a thousand random voices crying 'anathema' in different keys and from different motives. But the devil's advocate seems to have overplayed his hand, for the Mormon church has grown and flourished despite the sometimes malicious tales told among the Gentiles." A large part of this anti-Mormon lore concerned the supposed evils of the church, and the sinfulness of Brigham Young and other Mormon polygamists. One of the 'best' of the several songs on the subject is*

"Brigham Young," which I learned from Dick Person of Cascade, Idaho. It dates back to at least 1868 when it was printed in a California songster.

Once, when I was singing at a quilting bee for the Daughters of the Utah Pioneers in Salt Lake City, a couple of the ladies asked me to "sing the song about Brigham Young." Thinking that it might perhaps be unsuitable for this group, I said I really didn't know it. But they said, "Oh, yes you do. We know you do because it's on one of your records." They told me, "We all know it," and proceeded to sing right along with me. One Mormon woman who learned the song in 1875 in Willard, Utah, recalled in 1946, "The (Mormon) young people often sang humorous and crazy songs like this when they rode home on horseback after the dances."

—R.S.

BRIGHAM YOUNG

As Sung by Rosalie Sorrels   *Traditional*

Brig-ham Young was a Mor-mon bold, The lead-er of the roar-ing ram, Shep-herd of a flock Of fine tub sheep And a pas-sel of pret-ty lit-tle lambs; And He lived with his five and for-ty wives In the ci-ty of the Great Salt Lake, Where they breed and swarm Like hens on a farm And they cac-kle like ducks to a drake. Brig-ham, Brig-ham Young, It's a mir-a-cle he sur-vived, With his roar-ing rams, And his pret-ty lit-tle lambs And his five and for-ty wives.

Brigham Young was a Mormon bold,
The leader of the roaring ram,
Shepherd of a flock
Of fine tub sheep
And a passel of pretty little lambs;
And he lived with his five and forty wives
In the city of the Great Salt Lake,
Where they breed and swarm
Like hens on a farm
And they cackle like ducks to a drake.

CHORUS:
Brigham, Brigham Young,
It's a miracle he survived,
With his roaring rams,
And his pretty little lambs
And his five and forty wives.

Number forty-five's about sixteen,
Number one is sixty and three,
And among such a riot
How he ever keeps 'em quiet
Is a downright mystery to me,
For they cackle and claw
And they jaw, jaw, jaw,
Each one has a different desire,
It would aid the renown
Of the best shop in town
To supply them with half they require.

CHORUS:
Brigham Young was a stout man once,
But now he is thin and old,
And I'm sorry to relate,
There's no hair upon his pate,
Where he once wore a covering of gold.
For his oldest wife won't wear white wool,
The young ones won't take red,
And in tearing it out
And taking turn about,
They have torn all the wool from his head.

CHORUS:
Now his youngest wives sing psalms all day,
The old ones all sing songs,
And among such a crowd
He had it pretty loud,
They're as noisy as Chinese gongs.
When they advance for a Mormon dance,
He is filled with the direst alarms,
For they're sure to spend the night
In a tabernacle fight
To see who has the fairest charms.

CHORUS:
Well, there never was a house like Brigham Young's,
So curious and so queer,
For his wives were double
And he had a lot of trouble,
And it gained on him year by year.
Now he sits in his state
And bears his fate
In a sanctified sort of way;
He has one wife to bury
And one wife to marry
And a new kid born every day.

CHORUS:

❖There is a large and growing Mexican-American population in the Snake River Basin that forms the border between eastern Oregon and western Idaho. This rich ethnic community is maintaining and creating a tremendous variety of cultural traditions — from the healing practices of los curanderos to the ritual celebrations marking the end of the onion harvest. A local corrido singer might describe the victory of a favorite horse at Les Bois racetrack, while norteño and conjunto bands mix and blend a wide variety of Mexican and non-Mexican influences.

This song is a unique val ranchera, which has been influenced by nuevo canto — the "New Song" of Mexico that deals with current issues in public life. "Soy Mexicano" ("I am Mexican") is a clear and natural statement about the difficulties of maintaining one's cultural identity while integrating into a foreign culture.

—R.S.

SOY MEXICANO

As Sung by Jose Basaldua, Adam Gonzales, Ernesto Basaldua, Rosalinda Guerra, Otilia Muñoz, and Rodrigo Menchaca

Musical transcriptions by David Kilpatrick and Lynette Hart

Soy un pobre mexicano
Con un dolor tengo de ser de mi raza
Porque ando solito buscando una vida
Pá hijos y mi madre y mi esposa querida.

Los gringos me dicen siempre que me miran
"¿Chicano que buscas?" Yo busco a mi vida.
Luego de ratito voltean y me dicen
"Siempre mexicano trae vida perdida."

Soy pobre y humilde y no me arrepiento
De buscar mi vida yo me averguenza.
Mis canción les canto a todos mis paisanos
No se les olviden que soy Mexicano.

Soy pobre Chicano bracero y unido
Con toda mi raza en Estados Unidos
Porque la pobreza me trajó a éstas tierras
En donde se dicen se encuentran riquezas.

Soy pobre y humilde . . .

I am a poor Mexican
With one sorrow, to be of my race
Because I am alone looking for a way of life
For my children, my mother, and my dear wife.

The gringos tell me every time they see me
"Chicano, what are you seeking?" I seek my life.
Later they turn around and tell me
"A Mexican always has a lost life."

I am poor and humble and I am not sorry
To look for my life, I am not ashamed.
I sing my song to all my compatriots.
Don't you forget that I am Mexican.

I am a poor Chicano, field worker and united
With all my race in the United States
Because poverty has brought me to this land
In the land where they say you find riches.

I am poor and humble . . .

◆ *This bolero extolls the beauties of the small city of Nampa, Idaho, where Santos Hernández lives and works. The love and respect for one's land and home,* *paramount virtues throughout Mexico, are evident in the lyrics.*
                                                 —R.S.

NAMPA

As Sung by Santos Hernandez   *Written by Santos Hernandez*

Nampa, Nampa Idaho
Tu tienes tu parque cubierto de flores
Nidito de amor
Nampa, Nampa Idaho
Tu tienes tus hembras cruzadas de indio
Y aquel gran Cuahtemoc que fue emperador
Nampa, Nampa Idaho
Pueblito querido donde he conocido
Mi primer amor.

Me voy, pero un dia volveré
En tus noches plateadas de luna
A platicar con mi amor.
(se repíte)

Nampa, Nampa Idaho
You have your park covered with flowers
Little nest of love.
Nampa, Nampa Idaho
You have your women descended from the Indians
And that great Cuahtemoc, who was emperor.
Nampa, Nampa Idaho
Dear little town where I met my first love.

I'm leaving, but one day I'll return
To your silvery moon nights
To talk with my love.
(twice)

VOLVER VOLVER

Es- te a-mor a-pas-ion- a- do An-da to- do al-bor-o- ta-do por vol-ver voy ca-mi- no al' lo-cu- ra Y'an que to- do me to- tur-a se que-rer. Nos de-jam-os ha-ce tiem-po Pe-ro me lle-gó el mo men-to de per-dér tu ten-ias mu- cha ra-zón L'e-go ca- so cor-a- zón Y me mue-ro por vol-ver Y vol-ver, vol-ver, vol-ver A tus bra- zos o- tra vez lle- ga- ré has- ta don- de es- tés Yo sé per- der, Yo sé per- der quier- o vol-ver, vol-ver, vol-ver.

Este Amor Apasionado	This tender and devoted lover
Anda todo alborotado por volver—	Feels completely ready and anxious to return—
Voy camino a la locura	I'm behaving as if I'm insane
Y anque todo me tortura sé querer.	And even though this tortures me, I know how to love.
Nos dejamos hace tiempo	We left each other some time ago.
Pero me llegó el momento de perdér.	But now my moment of loss has arrived.
Tu tenias mucha razón	You had every reason (to leave).
Le hago caso al corazón—	(But) I pay attention to my heart
Y me muero por volver—	And I'll die in order to return
Y volver, volver, volver	And return, return, return
A tus brazos otra vez—	Into your arms once again.
Llegaré hasta donde estés	I will find you wherever you are.
Yo sé perder, yo sé perder	I know how to lose, I know how to lose
Quiero volver, volver, volver.	I want to return, return, return.

(Translated by Tanya Gonzales)

66

Santos Hernandez: There are a number of corrido singers in the Snake River Valley. They sing about the lives of Mexican people: their loves, their deaths, their hardships. Santos Hernandez is well known throughout the area as one of the best corrido writers because his songs express these feelings in personal terms.
(Photo courtesy of Michael Cordell)

Oregon Shortline Engine 613.(Photo courtesy of Idaho State Historical Society)

WAY OUT IN IDAHO

B R A G G E R S , S K I N N E R S , & B O O M E R S

I'm the man who found Lost River, boys
And made Round Valley round.
I dug the Sweet, the deep-sea Sweet
That bittered that little town.
I dug the Boise Basin
And also old Caldwell
And I brought the Seven Devils
All the way from Hell.

Jack Trueblood

After the discovery period in the West came the steady settling period. There were grabbers, adventurers, railroad boomers, and horse skinners—and there were those who were in for the long haul. A lot of people came to take what they could get and stayed because they couldn't get out. But many came to stay in the first place. They built railroads, staked claims, and set up camps. Land was easy to come by but hard to live on. The songs and stories in this section reflect the challenges of travel through the high desert and mountains as well as the adaptation of popular tunes and lyrics to the local landscape.

Unfortunately, only a handful of the songs of the railroad builders have come down to us, but one of the best of these is this ballad of the narrow gauge railroad construction workers in Idaho. A great percentage of the track laid by the Oregon Short Line (now the Union Pacific) through Idaho and Oregon was only three feet wide (compared to the standard gauge of four feet, 8-1/2 inches) and there are still a few narrow gauge appendages to main trunk lines to be found (though unused) in Idaho.

"Way Out in Idaho" is a ballad complaint about bad working conditions, lousy food, and poor quarters, sharing both sentiment and some few lines with the best of the Arkansas complaint songs, "The State of Arkansas."

I learned this song from Blaine Stubblefield, whose comments about the song I have also included. There are a number of versions but two basic endings: in one, the speaker says he will earn a grubstake and get married elsewhere, then return to Idaho; in the other, the speaker vows to leave the state and keep right on going.

—R.S.

Now this man Kilpatrick that I mentioned in there—I have met some old timers in this country who knew that man. He was a contractor way back in the early days—I suppose back toward the Civil War. And also you heard the term 'man catcher' in there, and that was a person who was sent out in advance of these construction jobs, and he slipped up on the boys around the saloons. And the way he trapped them into it, they needed five dollars right now, so he paid them the advance if they would get on the train within a certain time, and some of them did. That's the song about Idaho.

—Blaine Stubblefield

WAY OUT IN IDAHO

As Sung by Rosalie Sorrels   *Traditional*

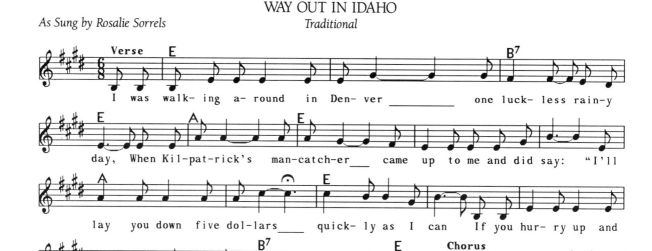

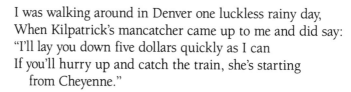

I was walking around in Denver one luckless rainy day,
When Kilpatrick's mancatcher came up to me and did say:
"I'll lay you down five dollars quickly as I can
If you'll hurry up and catch the train, she's starting
    from Cheyenne."

CHORUS:
Way out in Idaho, way out in Idaho,
A-workin' on the narrow gauge way out in Idaho.

Well he laid me down five dollars, like many another man,
And I hurried to the depot as happy as a clam;
When I got to Pocatello my troubles began to grow,
I was waitin' in the sagebrush . . . the rain, the wind, the snow.

CHORUS:
When I got to American Falls, it was there I met Fat Jack,
He kept a little hotel tent along beside the track.
"Now," says he, "You are a stranger, perhaps your funds are low,
Well, yonder stands me hotel tent, the best in Idaho."

"Spud Special" at Payette Depot, 1940. (Photo courtesy of Idaho State Historical Society)

CHORUS:

I followed my conductor into his hotel tent,
And for one square and hearty meal, I paid him my last cent.
Now Jack's a jolly fellow, you'll always find him so,
A-working on the narrow gauge, way out in Idaho.

CHORUS:

Well, they put me to work next morning with a cranky
    cuss called Bill.
They gave me a ten pound hammer to strike upon a drill;
They said if I didn't like it, I could take my shirts and go,
And they'd keep my blankets for my board way out in Idaho.

CHORUS:

Well, it filled my heart with pity, as I walked along the tracks,
To see so many old bundlers with their packs upon their
    backs;
They said the work was heavy, the grub they could not go
Around Kilpatrick's dirty tables way out in Idaho.

CHORUS:

Well, now I'm well and working down in the harvest camps,
And there I will continue till I make a few more stamps;
I'll go back to New Mexico, marry a girl I know,
And we'll buy us a horse and buggy and go back to Idaho.

❖ *Johnny Carrey of Riggins is one of the great story tellers we met on our exploration of Idaho's people. He told me of Idaho Jack Treadwell, who taught him the Bragging Song. I hope with this publication we'll find out more about the elusive blind fiddler whose fiddle Johnny Carrey still has and treasures.*

John Carrey heard Idaho Jack (Treadwell) sing this song at Clem Blackwell's pool hall.

I also learned another verse from Jack Trueblood, who learned it in 1969 at the U.S. Forest Service bunkhouse in Lowman from Frank Simmons, a horse-packer. Jack says Frank had "worked on every National Forest in Idaho" and "could have picked this verse up anywhere but claimed he wrote it." This claim fits with the character of the song! —R.S.

IDAHO JACK'S BRAGGING SONG

As Sung by Johnny Carrey

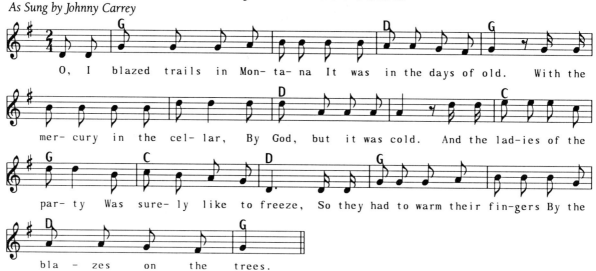

O, I blazed trails in Montana
It was in the days of old . . .
With the mercury in the cellar
By god, but it was cold . . .
And the ladies of the party
Was surely like to freeze . . .
So they had to warm their fingers
By the blazes on the trees.

The queerest sight I ever seen,
It made my blood run cold . . .
When Chief Joseph chased the soldiers
All down in Jackson's Hole . . .
It was in an Indian battle
When I heard the fierce war cry . . .
Where the pistols were a poppin
And the tommy hawks did fly . . .

I'm the man who found Lost River
And I also dug Cald-well . . .
I met the Seven Devils
And I drove them off to hell . . .
I removed the Grime from Grime's Creek . . .
Put the rocks in Rocky Bar . . .
And I made Payette pay up their debts
And then moved up to Star.

Watched Bigfoot skate in Boise Basin . . .
Followed his muddy track . . .
Up and down the mountains . . .
To the panhandle and back . . .
Oh, I have lived a good life
And I'll give the good Lord thanks . . .
And be a pal to my gal Sal
On the Salmon River banks.

72

In Grangeville we met Johnny Carrey — author, storyteller, great rememberer, and friend. We visited him later in Riggins and interviewed him about the history of everyone from Sylvan Hart to Polly Bemis. It's hard to leave Riggins if you get into a yarn session with Johnny. (Photograph by Michael Cordell)

This song was written in Round Valley about 1927. We had an Edison portable phonograph with cylinder records. Idaho Jack especially liked the record "The Wreck of the Old '97." He decided to write a parody of it using the same tune and honoring the old Freighter of the West that went to remote mining towns where the railroads never did go. He felt that these old freighters had rendered a very important service in the early days of our country and should not be forgotten. Idaho Jack was always a very welcome guest in our home when he would come like a wandering minstrel of the middle ages singing his songs and reciting his poems. He was the most interesting, unusual, and talented character that I have ever known.

—Mrs. Wilma L. Callander (Riggins)

THE LONG LINE SKINNER
(To the tune of: "The Wreck of the Old '97")

One June morning in the early sixties
When the western states were new
All freight was hauled by a long line skinner
Ere the big iron horse came through.
An outfit hitched and the wagons loaded
Waiting for daylight
With a barrel on tap in the old trail wagon
And a ton of dynamite.
The skinner puffed like a locomotive
At a pipe between his lips
While a shot-whip hung like a great dark serpent
From his shoulders past his hips.
Twenty thousand was the bill of lading
That he held before his eyes
He turned a black bottle right up to the heavens
And he bid the town goodbye.
He climbed to the back of his high wheeler
And his voice spoke low and droll.
Twelve big "neds" then leaned in the collar
And the wheels began to roll.
He tried his brakes at the top of the mountain
And everything looked well.
He set the lever 'way up the rachet
And started down Wildcat Hill.
He was going down grade with a slack in his rigging
Just a few short miles from home
While his name bells chimed to the step of his leaders
And his brake blocks shrieked and moaned.
Something snapped without any warning—
The wagons rushed onto the teams.
In a loud clear voice he called to his leaders
And his whip cracked loud and keen.
He was self-possessed in a time of danger;
He was noted for his skill—
And well he knew that his only chance
Was to run that Wildcat Hill!
His wheelers were braced well back in the rigging—
His leaders fouled in the chain.
He tried and tried to bank his wagon
But his efforts were in vain.

It was half a mile to a sandy bottom
Where a stop might safe be made—
On a short, sharp curve the tongue
 snapped like a splinter
And his wagons left the grade.
No more will his name bells announce his coming
For death has stilled their chime.
He was found beneath the old trail wagon
With his hand still on the lines.
Ladies dear, speak more kindly—
Don't let your voice be stern.
Don't get hard-biled with your long line skinner
Or he may leave you and never return.

❖ *Under the terms of the Homestead Act of 1862, a man could claim 160 acres of land provided he lived on the land and worked the claim for five years: "I've got a little bet with the government," the old homesteader might say, "They're betting me I can't live here for five years and I'm bettin them I can." I've heard that homesteading started in the midwest then extended all over the country, but it still goes on way out in Idaho.*

—R.S.

LITTLE OLD SOD SHANTY ON THE CLAIM
(To the tune of "The Little Old Log Cabin in the Home")

I am looking rather seedy now, while holding down my claim,
    And my victuals are not always of the best,
And the mice play slyly round me as I nestle down to rest
    In my little old sod shanty on the claim.

CHORUS:
The hinges are of leather and the windows have no glass
    While the board roof lets the howling blizzard in,
And I hear the hungry coyote as he sneaks up thru' the grass
    'Round my little old sod shanty on the claim.

Yet I kind of like the novelty of living in this way,
    Though my bill of fare, at times, is rather tame;
But I'm happy as a clam on this land of Uncle Sam
    In my little old sod shanty on the claim.

But when I left my eastern home, a bachelor so gay,
    To try to win my way to wealth and fame,
I little thought that I'd come down to burning twisted hay
    In my little old sod shanty on the claim.

My clothes are plastered o'er with dough, and
    I'm looking like a fright.
And everything is scattered round the room;
    But I wouldn't give the freedom that I have out in the West
For the bauble of an eastern mansard home.

Still I wish that some kind-hearted girl would pity on me take,
    And relieve me from the mess that I am in.
The angel, how I'd bless her, if this her home she'd make
    In my little old sod shanty on the claim.

And when we made our fortune on the prairies of the West,
    Just as happy as two lovers we'd remain.
We'd forget the woes and troubles which we endured at first,
    In our little old sod shanty on the claim.

And if the fates should bless us with now and then, an heir,
    To cheer our hearts with honest pride to flame,
Oh, then we'd be content for the toil that we had spent
    In the little old sod shanty on the claim.

When time enough has lapsed and all those little brats
    To man and modest womanhood have grown,
It won't seem half so lonely when around we can look
    At the other old sod shanties on the plain.

STARVING TO DEATH
ON A GOVERNMENT CLAIM
(To the tune of "The Irish Washwoman")

Frank Baker's my name, and a bachelor I am.
I'm keeping old bach on an excellent plan.
You'll find me out west in the county of Lane.
A-starving to death on a government claim.

My home is constructed of natural soil.
The walls are erected according to Hoyle.
The roof has no pitch, but is level and plain,
And I never get wet till it happens to rain.

Hurrah for Lane county, the land of the free,
The home of the grasshopper, bedbug, and flea!
I'll holler its praises, and sing of its fame
While starving to death on a government claim.

How happy I am as I crawl into bed.
The rattlesnakes rattling a tune at my head,
While the gay little centipede, so void of all fear,
Crawls over my neck and into my ear;
And the gay little bedbug, so cheerful and bright,
He keeps me a-going two-thirds of the night.

My clothes are all ragged, my language is rough.
My bread is case hardened, both solid and tough.
My dough is scattered all over the room,
And the floor would get scared at the sight of a
  broom.

The dishes are scattered all over the bed,
All covered with sorghum and government bread.
Still I have a good time, and I live at my ease
On common sop sorghum, and bacon an' cheese.

How happy I am on my government claim.
I've nothing to lose, I've nothing to gain.
I've nothing to eat and I've nothing to wear,
And nothing from nothing is honest and fair.

Oh, here I am safe, so here I will stay.
My money's all gone, and I can't get away.
There's nothing to make a man hard or profane
Like starving to death on a government claim.

Now come to Lane county, there's room for us all,
Where the wind never ceases and the rains never
  fall.
Come, join in our chorus to sing for the fame,
You sinners that're stuck on your government
claim.

Now, hurrah for Lane county, where the blizzards
  arise,
The wind never ceases and the moon never rises,
Where the sun never sets, but it always remains
Till it burns us all out on our government claims!

Now, don't get discouraged, you poor hungry men.
You're all just as free as the pig in the pen.
Just stick to your homesteads, and battle the fleas
And look to your Maker to send you a breeze.

Hurrah for Lane county, the land of the West,
Where the farmers and laborers are ever at rest;
There's nothing to do but to stick and remain,
And starve like a dog on a government claim.

Now all you poor sinners, I hope you will stay
And chew the hard rag till you're toothless and
  gray.
But as for myself, I'll no longer remain
To starve like a dog on this government claim.

Farewell to Lane county, farewell to the West.
I'll travel back east to the girl I love best.
I'll stop at Missouri and get me a wife,
Then live on corn dodgers the rest of my life.

David, Dennis and Thomas Johnson.
(Photo courtesy of Idaho State
Historical Society)

Willis Hansen, rawhider.
(Photograph by Gary Stanton)

Blanche Cowger showed up at an afternoon visit to the senior citizen's center in Kooskia. She showed me her scrapbook of songs she's collected for years and the next thing we knew, we were in her trailer livingroom sharing stories and songs with her friends in one of the most memorable afternoons of our trip. (Photo courtesy of Michael Cordell)

❖ *Songs like this one are sung with great fondness and romanticize the railroad as a way of travel. The late, great Jimmie Rodgers made the song "All Around the Water Tank" out of "10,000 Miles Away from Home" and other lonesome hobo songs. This version is from Blanche Cowger of Kooskia.* —R.S.

THE HOBO'S SONG

As Sung by Blanche Cowger

Hangin' 'round the water tank,
   Waitin' for a train,
A thousand miles away from home,
   Sleepin' in the rain.

I walked up to the brakeman
   To shoot him a line of talk.
Says he, "If you've not money,
   I'll see that you don't walk."

I haven't got a nickel,
   Not a penny can I show."
"Get off, get off, you railroad bum,"
   And he slammed that boxcar door.

He put me off in Texas,
   The state I dearly love,
With the wide open spaces all around
   And the moon and stars above.

Nobody seemed to want me,
   Or give me a helping hand;
I'm on my way from Frisco
   Gettin' back to Dixie land.

My pocketbook is empty,
   My heart is full of pain,
A thousand miles away from home,
   I'm swingin' the next freight train.

*Roland, Idaho, 1920's.
(Photo courtesy of
Barbara Germaine)*

❖*Collected at the Wallace song swap, this song was written by Kate Guehlstorff for the Centennial Celebration of Wallace's Northern Pacific Train Depot on September 26, 1987. Here's what Kate had to say when she last wrote me a letter: "In July of 1987, Mike Green at the Northern Pacific Railroad Museum called me and asked me to write a song for their Depot's centennial celebration . . . He sent me a wonderful article that he had written about the Depot's history and I basically worked from that. It was never intended to be a fancy song, but one that would be easy to sing along with at the event. When we performed in Wallace . . . I was touched that so many folks there liked it and were able to sing along with us. And here I thought that it was just a one-event song! Needless to say, we had a lovely time . . ."* —R.S.

BEEN RAILROADING NOW FOR 100 YEARS

As Sung by Kate Guehlstorff   Written by Kate Guehlstorff

(1.) If on-ly this de-pot could re-tell the tale of a time long a-go when they brought out by rail A new town with new hopes and lead sil-ver dreams. The time has passed quick-ly it seems. (2.) The nar-row gauged Coeur d'A-lene was the first rail-way line To link up our com-mun-i-ty with those down the line. Then came the de-pot built in nine-teen-o-one North-ern Pa-cif-ic would see the work done. We've been rail-road-ing now for one hun-dred years. We cel-e-rate our his-to-ry with laugh-ter and tears. We re-mem-ber both the hard times and good long a-go. We're the rail-road-ing sil-ver king, Wal-lace, I-da-ho.

Wallace Depot.
(Photo courtesy of
Mike Green)

If only this depot could retell the tale
Of a time long ago when they brought out by rail
A new town with new hopes and lead silver dreams.
The time has passed quickly it seems.

The narrow gauged Coeur d'Alene was the first railway line
To link up our community with those down the line.
Then came the depot built in nineteen-o-one
Northern Pacific would see the work done.

CHORUS:
We've been railroading now for one hundred years.
We celebrate our history with laughter and tears.
We remember both the hard times and good long ago.
We're the railroading silver king, Wallace, Idaho.

This depot's withstood all the hardships of time,
Seen fire and flood and wrecks on the line.
With rare bricks from China, and roots in the mines
Wallace's depot still shines.

CHORUS:
The rails are near gone now but still there remains
This grand old brick depot to honor those trains
To hold up our memories and show us the way
Back to those old glory days.

CHORUS, TWICE:

❖Hannibal F. Johnson, known as "Seven Devils" Johnson, was one of the early day mining men of the Seven Devils mining boom. He was born in Indiana in 1830 and crossed the plains with his parents by covered wagon. He was a freight packer in the Boise Basin during the 1860's. In 1892, he located the Eldorado Group of mines on Rapid River and established a permanent home there. He also was a poet and a writer, served in the State Legislature, and carried on a large correspondence, both political and social. I have included his poem, "A Trip to Rapid River," because of the picture it gives of life in Idaho during the period from about 1850 to about 1916 when Mr. Johnson died.
—R.S.

A TRIP TO RAPID RIVER
by Hannibal F. Johnson

1.

It was on the twenty-fifth of March, eighteen hundred and ninety-two,
There met in Council Valley a jolly mining crew;
Three of them from the Webfoot State, the other three we know
Had lived for many years within the State of Idaho.

CHORUS:
You hear of Rapid River! You take the golden fever!
Got a pretty girl at home? Go right away and leave her.
Saddle up your old cayuse and through the valley go it;
And if you strike a good thing, let everybody know it.

2.

We were bound for Rapid River, we scarcely had a dime;
It was just before the rush began, the weather was sublime;
But now the snow is melting fast, the mud is to our knees;
Before we reached the camp that night, I thought we'd surely freeze.

3.

We reached the Salmon Meadows, the snow was very deep;
The Webfooters took a cutoff, which almost made them weep;
They'd traveled many hundred miles and at great expense,
And in the Salmon Meadows had to coon a barbed wire fence.

4.

Then down the Salmon Meadows, through mud, ice, and snow;
The road turned out so very bad we had to travel slow.
We reached a Mr. Campbell's, a place we all admire;
We found a spot where we could squat and build a small campfire.

5.

Early in the morning, the earth was white with snow;
But soon the rain began to fall and that was forced to go.
The drizzling rain and chilling blasts made every member shiver,
But nothing could our zeal surpass; hurrah for Rapid River!

6.

Early after breakfast, we loaded up our train;
In disregard of wind and storm, we hit the road again;
We crossed the Little Salmon from east to western side;
We crossed Round Valley on a charge and hit the mountain side.

7.

Before we reached the summit, we had a small mishap;
Though nothing very serious, 'twas strange to Webfoot chaps;
The snow was four to six feet deep; with all our care and skill,
Our pack horse slipped upon the trail and tumbled down the hill.

8.

At last we crossed the summit, we did not this regret,
For still the rain was falling fast and everything was wet.
We reached the Little Salmon, we left the snow behind;
Here wood and water's plenty, but grass we could not find.

9.

Our ponies all seemed restless, they did not like the camp;
The grass so short and very scarce, they thought they'd take a tramp;
They waked us from our slumbers before the break of day;
We had to tie the leaders up and feed them on stake hay.

10.

We packed up in the morning and left that camp with speed;
We had to camp quite early to let our ponies feed;
The wind and snow and rain that night made every muscle quiver,
But still we kept the music up; hurrah for Rapid River!

11.

But still some distance we must go before we reached the camp,
Across the mountain through the snow, ten miles we had to tramp;
But courage boys, the end is near, and fortune will deliver
All those who scale the mountain peaks that border Rapid River.

12.

And now we've reached the golden shore; the mines are rich, no doubt.
We'll run our tunnels, sink our shafts, and take the ore out,
Then when we make our fortunes, we'll end this toil and strife;
We'll go back home, we'll wed our girls, and live a happy life.

❖❖❖

❖*The composer of this song, Mrs. Sarah Sullway Durant, writes in her letter that, "This poem was written especially for the* Scrapbook History Of Elmore County *which brought back so many pleasant memories for the poet."* —R.S.

ELMORE COUNTY SERENADE

Sing on the top of our mountains,
   Sing in the valleys below,
Deep in our evergreen forests,
   Forever the songs that we know.

Sing us a song of the prairie,
   Of the county we know and love,
Of the sagebrush that grows on the prairie,
   And the moon and the stars above.

Sing us a song of the pioneer,
   Of the family, wagon and team,
Of their faith and hope and fortitude,
   Of his planning and building a dream.

All will remember the songs that were sung,
   Of the pioneer men of yore,
And be inspired to work for their dreams,
   As our pioneers did before.

Now,
Our rivers are harnessed for power,
   The waters flow out to the scene,
Where planes in the air are landing,
   Out on the desert, now green.

So sing your songs and sing them loud,
   And sing them far and wide,
And all who hear will be cheered along,
   To new faith, new hope and new pride.

North Idaho loggers. (Photo courtesy of Idaho State Historical Society)

JACK-OF-ALL-TRADES
SONGS AND STORIES OF WORK

I'm a Jack-of-All-Trades
And a master of none,
I guess that's why I'm always broke,
And out of the mon.

Lyle Hall
Malad, Idaho

The people who came West to settle in Idaho had to be Jacks of All Trades. They had to know how to do everything — how to build a house, pull up stumps, irrigate the land, grow food, stack hay, make butter, sew clothes, tan leather, and make shoes. There was no one else to call upon and if the settlers didn't know how to do these things, they had to learn how or die.

It was like this with my grandparents, James Madison Kelly and Arabelle Beaire Kelly. Somewhere around 1914, they moved to Twin Falls, Idaho, and bought a ten-acre tract and began to farm it. Mr. Kelly built a small house to shelter his family and painted it brown. They called it "The Little Brown House" after the house in "Five Little Peppers and How They Grew."

My grandfather died when I was eight, but I remember him better than anyone I ever met — a handsome Irish face with piercing raven eyes alive with intelligence and humor. He was a literate man and cursed the horses in Shakespearean language: "The devil damn thee black, thou cream-faced loon!" (This with a snap of the reins to the rump of the sorrel with the white-blazed face.) I remember him singing, too, mostly when he separated the milk — "Old Dog Tray," "Run, Mary, Run" (a song he must have learned when he was a roustabout for minstrel shows that traveled from Ohio, where he was born, to as far south as Louisiana) and something about "doom, black doom" from a German ballad about a man who loved to hear mermaids singing.

My grandfather worked at a lot of jobs, traveled to far-flung places, went to the Alaska gold rush. He brought my grandmother out to that high plain in Twin Falls, where the wind blows down like the hounds of hell, and they farmed first ten, then twenty acres until he died. I never knew the official cause of his death. It's always been my gut understanding that he died of work.

Arabelle Beaire was a pretty woman, small-boned and graceful with an elegant steel-spined carriage. She was born in West Virginia and was the head nurse in Christ Hospital in Charleston before my grand-

father brought her West.

He wrenched a living from the land with old-fashioned machinery drawn by horses, butchered his own hogs and beef, harvested his own crops, never stopped to rest. She made the butter, made the soap, baked the bread, and canned the produce. Jams and jellies sat in rows on the shelves with relishes and pickles. She hooked the rugs and sewed all the clothing. She used every scrap of cloth and every bit of string too short to save for something else. She created beautiful tatting and cut work, crocheted tablecloths. Quilts and comforts graced every inch of that house. She had four gardens and somewhere close to 350 chickens to tend. Both of them got up before dawn and worked 'til they dropped every day of their lives, yet the values of serious thought, literature, poetry, and music inform every corner of my childish memory.

There was no money to buy anything in those days. People had to create their own beauty, making it from their own lives.

D.H. Lawrence said in his poem "Work" that each of us should like what we do:

> When a man goes out into his work
> He is alive like a tree in spring,
> He is living, not merely working.

But it was not like that for the Idaho pioneers. For them, work was more like Hannah Arendt described it in "The Human Condition" — relentless repetition.

To make all this awful work more bearable and to bring some beauty into their lives, the early settlers made up songs and sang them while they worked. Of course, my memories — the memories of my grandfather singing as he went about his work — are pleasurable ones. It is these songs — the folk songs, the songs of the people — that represent that spirit and that determination that still exists in Idaho people today. And songs are still being made. And for much the same reasons.

Many of the songs and stories we collected during our song swaps illustrate the diverse abilities of those who work on the land. What I find so impressive about the men and women who practice these skills is not only that they can learn so many different types of work, but that they can do them so well. The song which follows reflects this diversity of experience. Lyle Hall wrote it in 1965 at his home in Malad. He writes, "I really am a 'Jack-of-Trades.' I have done all these things."

—R.S.

JACK OF ALL TRADES

Written by Lyle Hall

I was born in Portage, Utah
Near the foot of Leavin Peak.
I used to go out hunting
At least once every week.
I recall when Dad would take me out
To see the rodeo . . .
He'd ride the buckin' broncos
And put on quite a show.

As I grew up I tried my hand
At every kind of work . . .
I've herded sheep and cattle
And I've been a soda jerk.
I've been a gandy dancer
On the D and RG line . . .
I went to Silver City once
And worked down in the mine.

I cut peaches down in Georgia
And cut wheat in Ioway . . .
I tended bar in Idaho
And worked out in the hay.
I strung my old guitar and sang
The songs about the West . . .
And when it comes to pickin' one,
That's what I love the best.

CHORUS:
I'm a jack of all trades
And a master of none. . .
I guess that's why I'm always broke
And out of the mon. . .
But I'm not complaining, folks
'Cause I've had my fun. . .
I'm a jack of all trades
And a master of none.

I put six years in the Navy
Where I helped to fight the Japs. . .
I worked for the ASCS
On photographs and maps.
At Thiokol I made rocket fuel
At Lazy Boy 'twas chairs. . .
These many talents I received
In answer to my prayers.

I've been a county mountie
And I've been a city cop. . .
At sellin' life insurance
I was a total flop. . .
I tried my hand at trappin'
And I worked at Crowther's Mill. . .
And I went to painting houses
And I'm at it still.

Horse drawn plow. (Photo courtesy of Idaho State Historical Society)

❖ *We found this song in the notebooks of three different people, including Blanche Cowger of Kooskia. People had saved it because of its importance to them as a celebration of the farmer. Wish we had the music for it.*
                                                   —R.S.

THE MAN BEHIND THE PLOW

I'm not so much at singing
  As those high-falutin' chaps.
My voice it may be husky
  And a little loud perhaps;
For I have been a-plowing
  With a lazy team, you see.
They kept one pretty busy
  With my "Giddup," "Whoa," "Haw," "Gee";
But if you pay attention
  I have just a word to say,
About a great mistake you make
  And do it every day
In dealing out your praise,
  And I want to tell you now:
Too often you forget the man
  That walks behind the plow.

CHORUS:
You talk about your learned men,
  Your wit and wisdom rare.
Your poets and your painters —
  They get praises everywhere.
They're well enough to make a show,
  But will you tell me how
The world would ever do without
  The man behind the plow.

It's very nice to go to school
  To learn to read and write;
It's nicer still to dress up fine
  And sport around at night;
Your "music," "painting," "poetry"
  May all be hard to beat,
But tell me what you're going to do
  For something good to eat?
You say my boots are muddy
  And my clothing is too coarse,
I make a good companion
  For the oxen or the horse;
My face is red, my hands are hard.
  It's true, I will allow,
But don't you be too quick to spurn
  The man behind the plow.

CHORUS:
I like your great inventions
  And I'm glad you're getting smart.
I like to hear your music,
  For it kinda stirs my heart.
But 'twould never touch the stomach
  Of a real hungry man.
And so I call attention to
  A kinda thing that can:
Then, boys, don't be too anxious
  For to leave the good old farm.
Your father's strength is failing,
  Soon he'll need your youthful arm.
If you're honest in your purpose,
  At your feet the world must bow,
For the greatest of the great men
  Is the man behind the plow.

CHORUS:

Mom was in her senior year of high school in Harlem, Montana, which is in the Milk River Valley. She was in the choir and she sang this song along with her two sisters, who were also in the choir. Here's the story that she tells about it:

Around the year 1921, the Billings Company contracted with some farmers from Idaho and brought them into the Milk River Valley to plant sugar beets. Now, as I understand it from hearing others talk, the sugar beets had come from France, I believe, and were tried in Idaho as an experiment and succeeded so well, apparently, that the Billings Company wanted the farmers to try them in Montana.

So they brought the farmers from Idaho, and Mom said as she remembers it, they were all LDS boys and their families. And the Montana farmers were settled in the Milk River Valley, which is quite a broad, beautiful valley through which the Milk River runs, and it is very close to the Bears Paw Mountains.

The Billings Company also contracted with the Great Northern Railroad to ship at least the first shipment of sugar beets from the fields to the factory with no charge to the farmers. They also asked the businessmen of Harlem to do everything they could to assist the farmers in starting their new farms, getting supplies, and so forth.

Now the businessmen agreed to do this, and they asked the high school choral director to put together some sort of nice party for the farmers. She planned a nice party, and it turned out to be a very special dinner followed by a lovely dance at which her choir performed the song that she wrote to commemorate the farmers coming to the Milk River Valley in Montana. She set the song to the tune of "The Glow Worm" and she had her choir sing it.

Now, there is a little pause which is not in "The Glow Worm" song itself where it comes in at "glow little glow worm, glimmer, glimmer" and in this song you'll hear a pause there where you're probably used to hearing a double word. The accompaniment took over the pause, so I'll just have to leave it. She called her song 'The Idaho Farmer' and here it is.

—Linda Crofts
Burley, Idaho

THE IDAHO FARMER
(Sung to the tune of "Glow, Little Glow Worm")

They have come from Idaho,
the state of Idaho
to seek their fortune
and if they should lose their way,
if they should lose their way,
the men of Harlem guide them with their friendliness,
their kindly friendliness
to build their homes there,
here and there and everywhere
in valley land with their riches,
building houses, barns and fences,
chicken coops and ditches.

Work little Idaho farmer (pause)
Work little Idaho farmer (pause)
Plant sugar beets for the Billings Company
The Great Northern Road will ship them free
Work little Idaho farmer (pause)
Now as the weather gets warmer (pause)
Smile and mix your work with pleasure
and good luck will follow you.

❖ *I first heard the expression "Cousin Jack" from Julie Tregaskis Kreiensieck. Tregaskis is a Welsh name. Nell and Vernon Henderson Tregaskis came into the Boise Basin in 1863. My mother, Nancy Stringfellow, says there were about thirty Welsh people in and around Idaho City and that they were called "Cousin Jacks." The reason was that whenever a good job opening would appear, the one already living there would say, "Hey, I'll send for my Cousin Jack!"*

Maidell Clemets of Osburn, who gave us this song, says the "Cousin Jacks" were London Cockneys.

—R.S.

MINERS AND MUCKERS TOGETHER
(To the Tune of "Sidewalks of New York.")

Miners and muckers together
Swedes, Norwegians, and Jews . . .
And old Cousin Jack
With a hump on his back . . .
A drink he would never refuse.

Miners here from Cornwall
Miners here from France . . .
Miners here from Coeur d'Alene
With the seat out of their pants.

Miners here from Missouri
Who never were under the ground.
Miners here who were drinking beer
When Puget was digging a sound.

Railroad tunnel workers.(Photo courtesy of Idaho State Historical Society)

THE SEVEN DEVIL MINES
By Hannibal F. Johnson
(To the tune of "Oh Susannah")

Come all ye bold adventurers
  and listen to my song
About the Seven Devil mines —
  I will not keep you long;
Those mines of wealth that's lately found
  Display the ore bright,
And millions yet beneath the ground
  Is bound to see the light.

CHORUS:
Then dig boys, dig, let us the ore find,
And open up in handsome style the Seven
  Devil mines.

And when you pack your old cayuse
  And start to make a raise,
And stop upon a grassy plot
  To let the equine graze,
You're liable at any time
  To meet a rattle bug,
Then don't forget the snake bite cure,
  Corked up in the brown jug.

Then when you reach the Devil mines,
  All filled with wind and gush,
Don't mope about and hang your head —
  You'd make the Devils blush;
But shoulder up your pick and pan
  And take your shovel too,
Then when you strike an ore vein,
  Just pop the Devils through.

And when the rock becomes so hard
  You can no longer pick,
Don't hang your head and look so sour —
  You'd make the Devils sick;
But seize your drill and hammer too,
  Put down a four-foot hole,
Then charge it well with dynamite,
  And let the thunder roll.

Then when we're down a hundred feet,
  With ore on the dump,
The money kings will all take hold
  And make the Devil's hump.
Then when we sell our mines of wealth,
  We'll money have to spend;
We'll put our plated harness on
  And visit all our friends.

Miners in ore car. (Photo courtesy of Idaho State Historical Society)

For when a man has wealthy grown,
  The past is all forgot;
He's honored, petted, loved and praised,
  Although a drunken sot.
And as our wealth accumulates,
  The ladies all will smile;
We'll bid the Devils a good-bye,
  And live in splendid style.

LAST CHORUS:
Then laugh boys, laugh, we have the ore found.
We'll make our pile, we'll live in style,
  Then pass the lager round.

❖ *George Venn of Eastern Oregon College at La Grande provided us with this song. He collected it from Mrs. Margaret Christian (Wallace) who noted, "The song was written by local men and was quite a hit fifty years ago." This song is inscribed, "To the miner, whose toil, friendship, joy and sorrow he has shared, this song is dedicated by its author."* —R.S.

SONG OF THE MINER

Music by Bert Simms

Lyrics by E.T. Cooke

We're just a bunch of hard rock men. We labor in the mines, Down in the dark earth's rock-y heart where the sun-light ne-ver shines. In shaft or stope in the raise or drift we toil from day to day, On morn-ing, night or the grave-yard shift, we try to make it pay: Good luck to the lad that digs the ore to the min-er of the West, His job is tough and his life is rough but he al-ways does his best. You may pros-pect near, You may pros-pect far, to the wide world's-dis tant end, and a rich-er strike you will nev-er make than a min-er for a friend.

We're just a bunch of hard rock men
We labor in the mines —
Down in the dark earth's rocky heart
Where the sun light never shines.

In shaft or stope, in the raise or drift,
We toil from day to day;
On morning, night, or graveyard shift,
We try to make it pay.

CHORUS:
Good luck to the lad that digs the ore
To the miner of the West.
His job is tough and his life is rough
But he always does his best.

The union's strong and the strikes are long
The silver's a mile deep.
He dreams of his ore and the mother lode
On his single-jack up the creek.

Burke, Idaho, 1900, showing Hecla mine. (Photo courtesy of Barnard-Stockbridge Collection, University of Idaho Library)

When the rounds are drilled and the timbers
   blocked
We load the holes and blast.
We can take a five on the sill perhaps
For the shift is in at last.

Then we crowd the deck of the waiting cage
The hoisting signals ring
As the cage climbs up through the smoky shaft
You can hear the miners sing.

CHORUS:
Good luck to the man who digs the ore,
The miner of the Coeur d'Alene.
His job is tough and his life is rough
And the company's half insane.

You may prospect near, you may prospect far
To the wide world's distant end,
And a richer strike you will never make
Than a miner for a friend.

When the parson gives the Lord three bells
And up the miner goes
To rustle at old St. Peter's gate
In his brand new digging clothes,

May he be most warmly welcomed
By the shift boss of the skies,
To the slopes of purest high grade
In the hills of paradise.

CHORUS:

May 2, 1972, in Kellogg, Idaho, started as a bright sunny morning. One hundred and seventy-eight miners were in some part of the complex of tunnels of the Sunshine Mine. Before noon fire broke out in the mine. Carbon monoxide, heat, smoke, and gasses filled many of the passaged areas, severely restricting rescue personnel. Eighty-five miners were able to escape early on. Seven days later, two more miners were found alive by the rescue crew. On the thirteenth, the last of the ninety-one victims was removed from the tunnels.

This was the worst hardrock mine disaster in the United States since 1917. The Sunshine Mine, which is more than a mile deep and has over 100 miles of tunnels, is the largest silver mine and producer in the free world.

On the second anniversary of the disaster the relatives and friends of the miners dedicated a memorial statue (twenty feet tall) on a large rock adjacent to the freeway and the mining property. The lamp on the miner's cap burns with an eternal flame. The entire memorial — from design through construction — was done by local people. The sculptor was a Sunshine employee.

Though this poem was written as the disaster progressed, as my own tribute to the Silver Valley Miners, it was not made public until 1983, out of respect for the families. Since I have worked in and around the local mines and was on a first name basis with more than half these men, I feel a great compassion for the families and personal loss myself.

—L. H. Harry
Pinehurst, Idaho

Sunshine Miners Memorial, Kellogg. (Photo courtesy of Robert McCarl)

SUNSHINE AND SORROW
By L.H. Harry

It was a beautiful day, that second of May,
    on the surface all was well!
Yet deep under ground, where the silver is found
    a mine fire was raising hell!

In the station a bunch had sat down to lunch.
    Their buckets and bottles were out.
They rested a while and died with a smile;
    That carbon monoxide had clout.

The men in the stope were left without hope,
    as the smoke in the tunnels grew thick.
Escape filled the mind as those left behind
    smelled the garlic and laid down their pick.

The toil in the mine is not ninety-nine fine
    like the silver refined from that hole.
The labor is rough and the laborer tough,
    Hard work, it's said, strengthens the soul.

Their bodies were found on the tracks and the ground
    The helmet crews searched every cranny.
When all hope was lost and they counted the cost
    The carnage was truly uncanny.

The two in the raise were not heard from for days,
    They had remained at the face of the wall.
As they came walking out mountains echoed the shout.
    That rescue team surely looked tall.

There have been stories told about sourdoughs and gold,
    and many about miners' wives.
This story, my friend, as it comes to an end,
    cost ninety-one miners their lives.

So always remember that second of May,
    and the "Jewel" with the smoke rising high.
Man's needs and desires plus runaway fires,
    caused ninety-one miners to die.

My grandfather, Melvin J. Snook, of Orofino (former logger, state senator, and postmaster) sent me these lyrics a couple of years ago. He suggested that I write some music for them. The lyrics were written in 1938 by Earl Neese of St. Maries, a sometime logger with literary ambitions. I tried to draw on traditional folk influences (both Scandinavian and Irish) to write the music. I picked up some of these tunes while living in northern Europe during the late 1970's. —J.J. Dion
Boise, Idaho

THE LOST LUMBERJACK

Music by J.J. Dion   *Lyrics by Earl Neese*

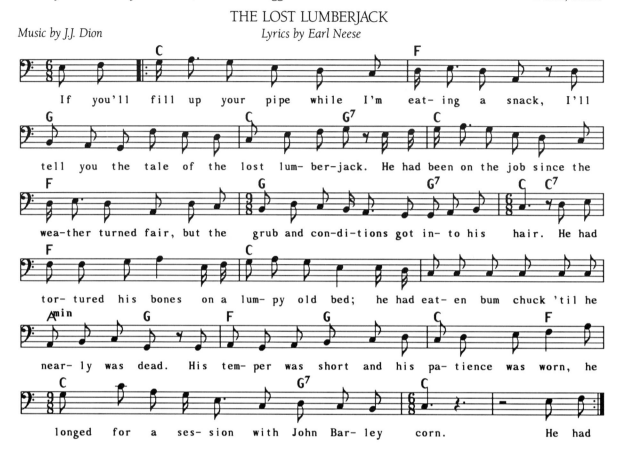

If you'll fill up your pipe while I'm eating a snack,
I'll tell you the tale of the lost lumberjack.
He had been on the job since the weather turned fair,
But the grub and conditions got into his hair.
He had tortured his bones on a lumpy old bed;
He had eaten bum chuck until he nearly was dead.
His temper was short and his patience was worn.
He longed for a session with John Barleycorn.
He had Sunday'd in camp to save up a stake,
But now he was tired of the whole cussed fake.
While doing his washing and mending his clothes
A tide of resentment within him arose.
He hated the Hoosiers that came off the farm.
He hated their lingo, their farmerfied yarns.
It seemed the old timers were all getting queer,
Forsaking the old things all loggers hold dear.
A shaggy old bear, who was playing a hunch,
Sneaked down to the skidway and grabbed his lunch.
Then he drowned his peavy and picked up his axe
And told the straw push a few simple facts.
He told him to take all his junk and haywire
And go to the place full of brimstone and fire.

He went to the office and drew his last check
And swore he'd quit logging forever, by heck.
He shouldered his packsack and hit down the track.
He was hitting the trail of the lost lumberjack.
He caught the first bus that would take him to town.
He would drink no more whiskey; he would not be a clown.
When he got to the city he would have a real feast
And would make resolutions that would honor a priest.
He would see no wild women, he would lay off the booze.
He would buy some good clothes and scow-bottomed shoes.
He went to a hotel and paid for a room
But when he got settled the place filled with gloom.
He went for a stroll and his pride took a fall
When he looked with regret at the Old Wobbly Hall.
He went to the skidway and who did he see
But just an old friend who had been on a spree
Whose tonsils were parched and he had a headache
So he bought him a drink just for old times' sake.
Right down on the bar his money he plunked,
And in less than an hour he was barrel-house drunk.
A few mornings after, when he awoke,
He had that queer feeling we have when we're broke.

Logger using peavey.
(Photo courtesy of Idaho
State Historical
Society)

So he went on the bum like the rest of the boys
And followed the ones who were having their joys.
When he had worked his last live one and mooched
  his last beer,
Then the world seemed to him like a place without cheer.
He was straining his wisdom to make a new find
When a copper approached him and made up his mind.
He towered before him and glowered a frown,
and told him with meaning to get out of town.
He shouldered his pack sack, caught a freight headed West,
Knew not where he was going, and cared a lot less.
He got ditched in the country where nature seems grand
With miles of sage brush and mountains of sand.
There he tried picking peaches, piling spuds up in heaps.
He worked for butcher and tried skimming sheep.
Then he read a want ad with a heavenly charm.
He could live close to nature and work on a farm.
But while milking the cows and feeding the hogs,
He remembered the pleasure he had had cutting logs.
He got up one morning with blood in his eye
And heaved the milk buckets inside the pig sty.
He shouldered his pack sack and hit out for town,
Where he bought him some licker, his troubles to drown.
He went to the jungles and had a few drinks,
And fell fast asleep while trying to think.
And when he awoke in a hot sultry breeze,
He cursed all the countries that didn't have trees.

He realized with horror, that while on his toot,
Some cold-hearted villain had stole his corked boots.
Then he went to a dump that the garbage men use,
There among the tin cans he found some old shoes.
The soles were wore thin and the walking was rough,
And he said to himself that he'd sure had enough.
He went to the yards in search of a freight,
And when he arrived, he hadn't long to wait.
He looked for an empty but none could he spy,
He grabbed a tank car that was just rolling by.
He scrambled aboard and grounded his pack.
He was hitting the trail of the lost lumberjack.
He hadn't a coat and his shirt was wore thin.
He soon realized he was out in the wind.
When she hit the high centers, she rolled like a whale,
And he clung for dear life to the chilly hand rail.
They were taking the curves at a hair-raising speed,
And that's when his pack sack rolled out in the weeds.
Well, he went back to camp and his travels were done.
He greeted the boss like a prodigal son.
The boss was a guy with a rough, tender heart.
He bore him no malice for playing his part.
He regarded his clothes with a comical grin,
And told him, "Why sure, he could always sit in."
Now in peace and contentment, real joys he can feel,
Until again overcome by the wandering heel.

An old Scottish bothy ballad, "The Barnyards of Delgaty," provided the tune for this lively Idaho lumberjack song. Like its logger descendant, the Scottish original was a wild boasting song with an infectious refrain. Perhaps some old woodsman, not so far removed from the Scottish soil, remembered the old song while hauling timber in the Idaho woods and set these rambunctious words to the tune.

—J. Barre Toelken

TOO REE AMA

As Sung by Barre Toelken

Traditional

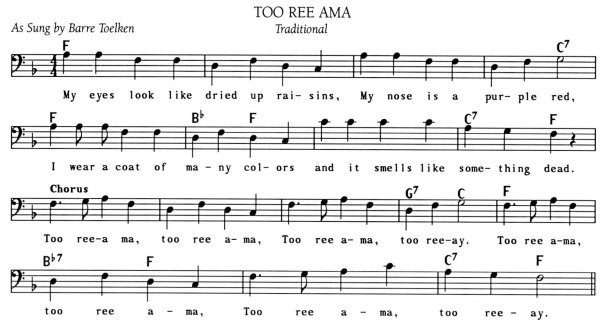

My eyes look like dried up rai- sins, My nose is a pur- ple red, I wear a coat of ma- ny col- ors and it smells like some- thing dead.

Chorus

Too ree-a ma, too ree a-ma, Too ree a- ma, too ree-ay. Too ree a-ma, too ree a - ma, Too ree a - ma, too ree - ay.

My eyes look like dried up raisins,
My nose is a purple red,
I wear a coat of many colors
And it smells like something dead.

CHORUS:
Too ree ama, too ree ama,
Too ree ama, too ree-ay.
Too ree ama, too ree ama,
Too ree ama, too ree-ay.

I can tame a wild hoot'nanny,
I can chop a redwood tree,
I dip snoos[1] and chew tobaccy:
Will you marry me, me, me?

CHORUS:
I went down to see my honey,
When I got there she was sick;
In her gut they found a peavy,[2]
Three pulaskis[3] and a pick.

CHORUS:
I can drink and not get drunken,
I can fight and not get slain.
I can kiss another man's girlie
And be welcome back again.

CHORUS:

[1]*snoos:* snuff
[2]*peavy:* stout, hooked pole for turning logs in the water
[3]*pulaski:* fire-fighting tools with an ax blade on one side of its head
and a narrow mattock on the other.

❖ *This fragment by J. Lish, dated October 1977, was discovered in a "fly shed" used by Forest Service employees during Ship Island Fire in 1979. John Carrey got it from Dick Hauff, supervisor of the Salmon National Forest.* —R.S.

There's nothing like a little cabin
to weather out a storm —
build a fire, plug up the door
and it will keep you warm.
Here's to the Forest Service —
my credit they do earn. Thank
you for this cabin that you
forgot to burn.

Cabin, Duck Valley Reservation.(Photo courtesy of Steve Siporin)

❖❖❖

❖ *The Ship Island fire was declared controlled at 10,480 acres on August 15. Suppression costs included one life and almost a million dollars.*

Those who boated through the 1979 "summer of fire" will never forget it. For two weeks, the smokey pall that obscured the afternoon sun cast an eerie, surreal light across the Middle Fork canyon. The feeling is best captured in portions of a poem by Scott Greer:—R.S.

All day the trees were heavy with flowers of smoke,
Their charred perfume of withered cones and needles
Stained the sombre skies we travelled under,
Tainting the light we knew, the air we breathed.

The burning oils of death had steeped the day;
Lightning had sown the green with a thousand seed
And heavy slopes returned their lives to the sun
In a sudden explosion of bright and mortal being.

— Dark illuminations in August noon;
Grey waves roiling, of wind and smoke,
Parted to a column of black through the dusk,
A great cone of mountain, a charred and dying slope.

As the forest was unburdened of its ghostly flowers
Their sweet and hopeless scent grew on the air,
On tongue and lips and eyes and it was neither
Catastrophe nor covenant nor prayer —

It was our nature cast against the Sun;
Our senses guttered in the terrible wind
As all the slow fuses went blazing, charred and one
With the ravager who soars towards the end.

— from *The Middlefork and the Sheepeater War*
By Cort Conley and Johnny Carrey

❖ *My aunt Ethel Summers Stringfellow got this poem from her friend, Marion Royer, who lives in Twin Falls. Ethel was active for years in an organization called the "Cowbelles." In the fifties, she was the Idaho secretary of this group that supported the Cattlemen's Association. Later, she was the Secretary Treasurer of the National Cowbelles under Mrs. Maxine Larsen. These women are mostly ranch women who support the use of beef and the welfare of the cattle industry.* —R.S.

ODE TO A COW
By Marion Royer

I used to think cows was dumb critters,
I figured 'em for stupid and slow;
But as I recollect back from my later years,
I gotta admit — I don't know!
'Pears to me that in most of our dealin's
The cow sorta had her say;
And though I mostly ended up being boss,
It didn't always turn out just that way.
I ain't layin' claim to no great intellect,
Or passin' for a genius now;
But I gotta admit that all that I know,
I learned from a doggone cow.

For nigh onto 40 years man and boy,
I've lived with them both night and day,
And the lessons I got while handlin' them cows,
You can bet I learned the hard way.
I've had the full course in psychology,
(I ain't sayin' who worked it on who)
As for language I've picked up a plenty,
Even some that turns the air blue.
My struggles with simple economics
Leaves me puzzlin' and wonderin' how
I always seem to sorta wind up
In lots worse shape than the cow.

She spends her days grazin' and loafin',
Peaceful and content with her lot.
She don't worry about interest or taxes,
Or the new car the neighbors just bought.
I guess you could say she's philosophical,
And I reckon some rubbed off on me;
'Cause in spite of all the ups and downs,
A cowman's what I'll always be.
But when I get to feelin' kinda down
I work long and hard to figure how
To really wind up convincin' myself
That I'm smarter than a doggone cow!

THE TENDERFOOT

As Sung by Helen Blume

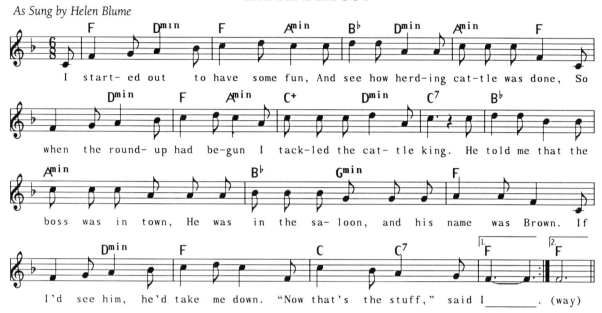

I start-ed out to have some fun, And see how herd-ing cat-tle was done, So when the round-up had be-gun I tack-led the cat-tle king. He told me that the boss was in town, He was in the sa-loon, and his name was Brown. If I'd see him, he'd take me down. "Now that's the stuff," said I_____. (way)

I started out to have some fun,
And see how herding cattle was done,
So when the roundup had begun,
I tackled the cattle king,
He told me that the boss was in town,
He was in the saloon, and his name was Brown.
If I'd see him, he'd take me down.
"Now that's the stuff," said I.

We went to the ranch the very next day.
Brown talked to me most all the way.
He told me herding cattle was play.
There was nothing to do at all.
It's just like drifting with the tide.
Oh, Jimminy Christmas, how he lied.
He certainly had his gall.

Next morning they saddled an old gray hack
And put a saddle upon his back
And padded him down with a gunny sack
And put on bedding and all.
When I got on, he left the ground.
He went in the air and he whirled around
And I fell down upon the ground
And that was a helluva fall.

They picked me up and they carried me in
And rolled me down with a rolling pin.
"Oh, that's the way they all begin, you're doing
    fine," says Brown.
"Now in the morning, if you don't die,
We'll give you another horse to try."
"Oh won't you let me walk," said I,
"Oh, yes, to town," said Brown.

They put me in charge of a calve yard
And told me not to work too hard.
There was nothing to do but ride.
When one would break, away we'd go.
Sometimes we'd head 'em and sometimes no.
My horse would stumble and then he'd fall
And I'd go on like a cannon ball,
Till the ground fell in my way.

I've traveled up and I've traveled down.
I've traveled the whole world round and round
And I have this much to say,
"Before you go to bunching cows,
Go across the plain, kiss your wife,
Insure your life, and shoot yourself with a
    butcher knife."
And that's the safest way.

❖ On his day off, or after a long trip on the trail, the cowboy would venture into town and make his rounds. And in the process of 'oiling up his insides', he frequently over-imbibed. The result might well be the incidents sung about in this wonderfully humorous and obviously fictional cowboy ballad.

The color and imagination of cowboy expressions has been commented upon frequently and in depth [see, for example, Ramon F. Adams' two fine works on the subject: Cowboy Lingo, (Boston, 1936), and Western Words, (Norman, Oklahoma, 1944)]. Perhaps the best of his expressions, and one which could successfully compete with the most colorful language created in any segment of American life, is the term "cowography," which simply means working with cattle.

This version comes from Barre Toelken.   —R.S.

SAWTOOTH PEAKS
("Tyin Knots in the Devil's Tail")

As Sung by Barre Toelken   *Written by Gail Gardener*

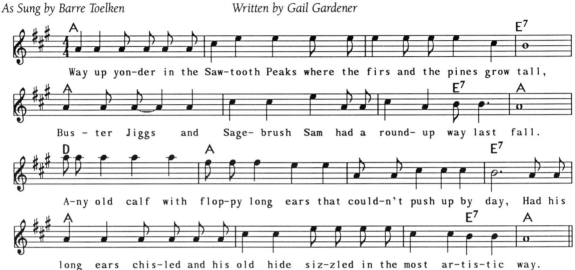

Way up yonder in the Sawtooth Peaks
where the firs and the pines grow tall,
Buster Jiggs and Sagebrush Sam
had a round-up way last fall.

Any old calf with floppy long ears
That couldn't push up by day
Had his long ears chiseled
And his old hide sizzled in the most artistic way.

Says Buster Jiggs to Sagebrush Sam
As he threwed his long legs down,
I'm a getting tired of cow-ography
So I reckon I'll jog to town.

They started out on right smart lope
For there weren't no sign of a rise,
Them was the days when the good cowboys
Would oil up their insides.

They headed down for Kentucky Bar
At the end of the Whiskey Row,
They wound up tight, later that night
Some forty drinks below.

Weigel's Saloon, Idaho City. (Photo courtesy of Idaho State Historical Society)

The house spun around and slapped them out,
So they started in the other way,
Honest to goodness, to tell you the truth,
Them boys got drunk that day.

They headed back for the Sawtooth Peaks
Just packin up a dern good load,
When who should they meet but the Devil Hisself
Come prancin' down the road.

"Confound you ornery cowboys,
Now you better had hunt you a hole,
Cause I'm the Devil from Hell's rimrocks
Come to gather up your soul."

"Now the Devil be-damned," says Buster Jiggs,
"Boys, you both know I'm tight,
But before you corral any cowboy soul,
You'll sure get a helluva fight."

Now Buster Jiggs was a lariat man
And his gut rope coiled up neat,
He dug him a hole and he threw him a roll
And he looped the Devil's hind feet.

They laid him down and they stripped him out
While the sizzle in the irons grew hot,
They trimmed his horns with a dehorn saw
And branded him a lot.

They tied ten knots in the old boys tail
Left him there for a joke,
With a beller and a cough old Jack took off
Out through the Black-Jack oak.

Now if you ever go ridin in the Sawtooth Peaks
And you hear a lonely wail,
It's only the Devil as he howls and prowls
With the knots tied in his tail.

103

❖ *Curley Fletcher, the giant of cowboy poetry, wrote this as a poem called, "The Flyin' U Twister." Blanche*   *Cowger sang it to us as a song.*   —R.S.

BAD BRAHMA BULL

As Sung by Blanche Cowger   *Written by Curley Fletcher*

I was snap-pin' out broncs for the old Fly-in' U At for-ty a
month a plumb good buck-a-roo. The boss comes a-round and he says "Say my
lad you look pret-ty good rid-in' hor-ses that's bad. You see I don't
have no more bad ones to break, but I'll buy you a tick-et and give you a
stake. At rid-in' them bad ones you're not so slow and you might do some
good at the big rod-e-o."

I was snappin' out broncos for the old Flyin' U
At 40 a month, a plumb good buckaroo.
The boss comes around and he says, "Say, my lad,
You look pretty good ridin' horses that's bad.
You see, I don't have no more bad ones to break;
But I'll buy you a ticket and give you a stake.
At ridin' them bad ones you're not so slow
And you might do some good at the big rodeo."

While they were putting the bull in the chute,
I was strappin' my spurs to the heels of my boots.
I looks the bull over and to my surprise,
There's a foot and a half, between his two eyes.
On top of his shoulders, he's got a big hump.
I cinches my riggin' right back of that lump,
I lights in his middle and lets out a scream.
He comes out a beller and the rest is a dream.

He jumps to the left but he lands toward the right;
But I ain't no green horn, I'm still sittin' tight.
The dust starts to foggin' right out of his skin;
A-wavin' his horns right under my chin.
At sunnin' his belly, he couldn't be beat;
A-showin' the buzzards the souls of his feet.
He's divin' so low my boots fill with dirt.
He's making a whip of the tail of my shirt.

He's snapping the buttons right off of my clothes;
A buckin' and bawlin' and blowin' his nose.
The crowd was a-cheerin' both me and the bull.
He needed no help while I had my hands full.
Then he goes steppin' slow and weavin' behind.
My head starts to snappin', I sorta went blind.
He starts to high divin', I let out a groan.
We went up together but he came down alone.

Up high I turn over and below I can see,
He's pawin' up dirt just a-waiting for me.
I can picture a grave and a big slab of wood,
Says here lays the twister that thought he was good.
Then I notices something can't seem to be true.
The brand on his hip is a big Flyin' U.
When he landed he charged but I got enough sense
To outrun that bull to a hole in the fence.

I dived thru that hole, and I want you to know
That I'm not going back to no Wild West show.
At strattlin' those Brahma's can bet I'm all thru.
I'm sore footin' it back to the old Flyin' U.

❖ *Betty Corrigan of Challis learned this song as a child from friends and family. "It's my understanding it came across the plains with the wagon trains and cattle drives," Betty says. She also tells us that her family has always sung and played music.* —R.S.

COWBOY JACK

As Sung by Betty Corrigan · *Traditional*

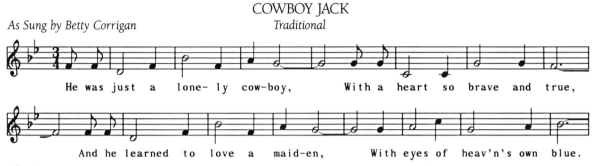

He was just a lone-ly cow-boy, With a heart so brave and true,

And he learned to love a maid-en, With eyes of heav'n's own blue.

He was just a lonely cowboy,
With a heart so brave and true,
And he learned to love a maiden,
With eyes of heaven's own blue.

They had learned to love each other,
And had named their wedding day,
When trouble came between them,
And Jack he rode away.

He joined a band of cowboys,
And tried to forget his name,
But out on the lonely prairie,
She waits for him the same.

One night when the work was finished,
Just at the close of day
Someone said "Sing a song, Jack,
That will drive dull care away."

When Jack began his singing
His mind it wandered back
For he sang of a brave true maiden
Who waited at home for him.

"Way out on the lonely prairie
Where the skies are always blue,
Your sweetheart waits for you, Jack,
Your sweetheart waits for you."

Jack left the camp next morning
Breathing his sweetheart's name,
"I'll go and ask forgiveness
For I know that I was to blame."

But when he reached the prairies
He found a newly-made mound.
And his friends they kindly told him
They had laid his loved one down.

Idaho buckaroo. (Photo courtesy of Idaho Commission on the Arts)

They said as she was dying
She breathed her sweetheart's name,
And said as with her last breathing
To tell him when he came:

"Your sweetheart waits for you, Jack,
Your sweetheart waits for you;
Way out on the lonely prairie
Where the skies are always blue."

105

Bill Simpson lives and works in the bends of Snake River Valley where he has written some of the most telling observations about cowboy life in his part of the country. His first book of poems, Listen Up, Pup *came out in 1985. (Photo courtesy of Michael Cordell)*

THE GLOW
By Bill Simpson

Well, what's in a fire
That pulls a man's desire
To stare a hard gaze
At a campfire blaze?

From the bright amber coals
To where the blue flame rolls,
The glow is sure there,
And it'll draw your stare.

Men set for hours
While the red flame flowers
Without a thought in their head,
Like their mind's gone dead.

No want and no care,
It'll just hold you there
In a blank state of mind
With nothing to find.

Well the poppin' and crackin'
Goes on unobserved,
It's the flames
That hold you so reserved.

They're leapin' and reachin'
And tryin' to find
A way to penetrate
Man's simple mind.

Jackson cooking near Lowman. (Photo courtesy of Idaho State Historical Society)

EARLY MORNING ROUNDUP
By Owen Barton

Have you ever saddled your horse
And been on your way,
When the hoot owls were hootin'
At the break of day?

And rode out on the range
In the real early morn,
And felt kinda' lucky
That you had been born?

Heard a meadow lark singin'
A real special tune,
With the stars fading out,
Though you can still see the moon.

Sagebrush and grass
Still sparklin' with dew,
The sky in the east is
Turning red, mixed with blue.

Your horse's shod hooves
Knock sparks from the rocks,
And you hear the strange struttin' sounds
Of them proud old sage cocks.

The lonesome wail
Of a coyote cry,
With nose pointed up
Toward the sky.

An eagle soars high,
With wings out-spread.
The sun's now coming up,
And it's sure big and red.

A red-tailed hawk screamin'
Down from the hill,
Looking for breakfast,
A rabbit to kill.

A magpie sits in a bush close by
Watching this with a watchful eye,
He'd like to enjoy a feast
With his brothers from the sky.

A horny toad struggles
To get out of your way,
A lizard glides off a rock
Like he wants to play.

Your horse shies off the trail
At the buzz of a rattle,
Then you sorta' remember
You're here to round up cattle.

Soon you jump some cows and calves
That take off on a run,
'Tis then you get to thinking
Cowboyin's nuthin' but fun.

Your horse is still fresh
And rarin' to go,
You're glad they are wild
And as yet ain't too slow.

You see an old bull bellerin'
And pawin' up dirt,
Then you take down your rope
To use as a quirt.

This is the way a roundup
Starts out on the range,
But along about noon
It all seems to change.

You've rode a big circle
Got them cows in a bunch,
You're breakfast's long gone
And you ain't got no lunch.

The sun sure is blazin'
Up high in the sky
You're lips are startin' to crack
They're gettin' so dry.

The water holes you've seen
Ain't fit to drink,
They're gettin' so stale
They're startin' to stink.

You still remember
That beautiful morn,
But the grin on your face
Has turned to forlorn.

You got the cows corralled
And have started to brand,
There's plenty of work
For every last hand.

The air's full of smoke
From the burnin' of hair,
And you're so damn tired
You don't even care.

Your throat starts to burn
From so much bitter smoke,
And your lungs fill with dust
'Till you think you will choke.

Owen Barton (left) and Bob Schild in Elko. (Photo courtesy of Steve Siporin)

Your hands are covered with blood
From earmarkin' ears,
And changin' bull calves
Into castrated steers.

Cows and calves bawlin'
In a loud steady roar,
It could only be louder
If there were more.

By the time the last calf
Is wearin' a brand,
You are dusty and sweaty
And your boots full of sand.

Then you open the gate
And let out a yell,
And they all stampede out
Like they were just leavin' hell.

Then you hold them in a bunch
'Till the calves find their mothers,
With a brand on the hip
They all look like the others.

But them old cows know
By the smell of the hide,
And each soon has her own
Trottin' off by her side.

You've darn near forgot
About that beautiful morn,
And how lucky you were
That you had been born.

Can't even remember
The meadow lark's song,
And you wonder how such a beautiful day
Could go wrong.

Your muscles all ache
And your butt's kinda sore,
But at daybreak tomorrow
You'll be ready for more.

You'll be wantin' to hear
That old coyote howl,
And watch the day break
At the hoot of an owl.

You'll again want to see
That old horny toad,
As he plows through the dust
To get out of your road.

Again see the eagle
As he soars in the sky,
And you'll hope you're a cowboy
'Till the day that you die.

109

❖ *"Camp Cook's Revenge" reminds me of Utah Phillip's wonderful story, "Moose-Turd Pie," about the gandy-dancer who escapes cook duty by baking up a "pasture pastry" and proclaiming that anyone who complains about the food has to be the cook. Humor is clearly the best way to deal with hard work, crumby conditions, and lousy pay.* —R.S.

CAMP COOK'S REVENGE
By E. Bruce Stanger

I took a job a-cookin'
On an outfit running cows.
Of all the jobs I ever took
This one took the cake for rows.

For the camp beef had gone rotten
And the flour it looked like sod.
The beans they were all ropey.
I swear they were, by Gawd.

So with chuck like that to cook with
And when the coffee tastes like tea,
The cowhands on that outfit
Was always mad at me.

So I thinks, "I'll fix them."
And show them no dude am I.
I'll make a pot of split pea soup
That'll make them cowboys cry.

It took half-a-pound of gun powder,
To give the stuff some grip.
Then a couple pounds of hot red peppers,
To make them fellers rip.

And a pound or two of cow pies,
Singed up to look like toast.
It smelt on high, clean up to the sky,
Clear past the Heavenly Host.

Well, them punchers came in hungry.
They was a looking for a fight.
"Come in, sit down," sez I,
"For I've made soup tonight."

With the first bowl, "Hey, Cook,
This soup, it tastes all right!"
But by the second go-round
The first one took its bite.

So they quick stepped down the table,
Kacked down their chaps and more.
And by the time them cuisined cowboys quit
They didn't ask me none for more.

So I checks my time and hoofs it down the line,
Just one step in front of the mob.
But, if you folks are a-lookin' for a camp cook,
I'm a-lookin' for a job.

Gene Autry, one of the all-time great cowboy singers and songwriters, wrote this ballad and copyrighted it in 1934. As a result of his successful recording of it, the song later appeared in various folios. Traditional cowboy ballads like this one favor the theme of death from an unexpected direction, although the death is usually the result of a cattle or horse stampede. The language, ideals, and mores of this ballad are in keeping with those we find in almost all authentic cowboy songs that have passed down to us during this century. The sentimentality commonplace in other cowboy songs is also evident in Autry's lines. This song is still being sung in Idaho some fifty-six years after its original composition. Rosalie learned it from Dick Person of Cascade, Idaho.

—Kenneth S. Goldstein

EMPTY COT IN THE BUNKHOUSE TONIGHT

As Sung by Dick Person   Written by Gene Autry

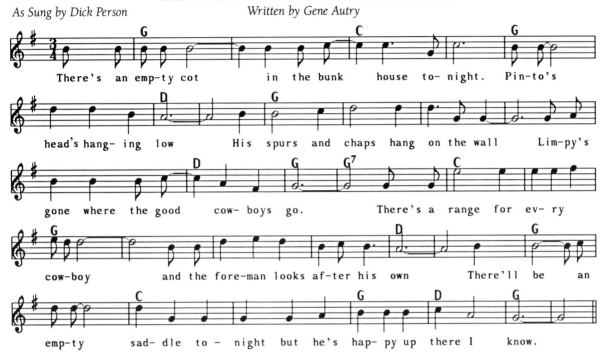

There's an empty cot in the bunk house to-night. Pin-to's head's hang-ing low His spurs and chaps hang on the wall Lim-py's gone where the good cow-boys go. There's a range for ev-ry cow-boy and the fore-man looks af-ter his own There'll be an emp-ty sad-dle to-night but he's hap-py up there I know.

There's an empty cot in the bunkhouse tonight.
  Pinto's head's hanging low;
His spurs and chaps hang on the wall:
  Limpy's gone where the good cowboys go.
There's a range for every cowboy and
  the foreman looks after his own.
There'll be an empty saddle tonight,
  but he's happy up there I know.

He was riding the range last Saturday noon,
  when a Norther started to blow,
With his head in his chest heading into the west,
  he was stopped by a cry soft and low;
There a crazy young calf had strayed from its maw,
  and lost in the snow and the storm,
It lay in a heap at the end of the draw,
  huddled all in a bunch to keep warm.

Limpy hobbled his feet, tossed him over his hoss,
  started again for the shack;
The wind blew cold and the snow piled high
  and poor Limpy strayed from his track.
He arrived at three in the morning
  and put the maverick to bed;
He flopped in his bunk not able to move,
  in the morning poor Limpy was dead.

There's an empty cot in the bunkhouse tonight,
  Pinto's head's hanging low;
His spurs and chaps hang on the wall,
  Limpy's gone where the good cowboys go.
There's a range for every cowboy
  and the foreman looks after his own,
And someday he'll ride old Pinto
  on the range up there above.

The setting was different, and so was the tune, but this ballad was sung in Ireland over 150 years ago. Then it was known as "The Unfortunate Rake," and it told the tale of a young man who died of too much high living . . . and some venereal disease. The song eventually travelled across the ocean and became known in various versions as "The Bad Girl's Lament," "The Streets of Laredo," "The Wild Lumberjack," etc., and was parodied many times more by occupational groups, students, union pickets, and others.

—Kenneth S. Goldstein

❖❖❖

❖We've all heard one version or another of this song, particularly the one beginning,

As I walked out in the streets of Laredo
As I walked out in Laredo one day . . .

There are versions, or parodies, of this same basic song recording the death of a college professor in West Los Angeles and the sad demise of a ski bum in Sun Valley, Idaho. All tell of the speaker's young vigor, sudden mishap, and the sometimes elaborate request for his funeral.

I collected this Burley version in 1958 from Russ Russell, a boomer lineman. The scare-strap, hooks and D-ring are all part of the pole-climber's rig. In other transcripts of this song, the speaker asks to "ring the phone softly," and that he be taken to "Kline, the Great White Father" — a high official in the Idaho Power Company at one time.

—R.S.

THE STREETS OF OLD BURLEY

As Sung by Rosalie Sorrels   Collected by Rosalie Sorrels

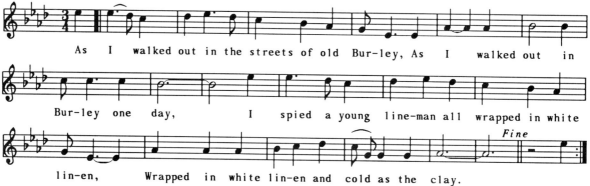

As I walked out in the streets of old Bur-ley, As I walked out in Bur-ley one day, I spied a young line-man all wrapped in white lin-en, Wrapped in white lin-en and cold as the clay.

Burley Land Office, 1905. (Photo courtesy of Idaho State Historical Society)

As I walked out in the streets of old Burley,
As I walked out in Burley one day,
I spied a young lineman all wrapped in white linen,
Wrapped in white linen and cold as the clay.

"I see by your scare-strap that you are a lineman,"
These words he did say as I boldly walked by.
"Come sit down beside me and hear my sad story,
I fell off the pole and I know I must die.

"'Twas once at the poles I used to go dashin',
Once at the poles I used to go gay,
First up the sixties and then up the nineties,
But I fell off an eighteen and I'm dyin' today.

"Oh, ring the boom softly and climb the pole slowly,
And check your D-rings when you go aloft,
Keep your hook sharpened and grease up your scare-strap,
I'm telling you, buddy, that ground ain't so soft.

"Get me six drunken lineman to carry my coffin,
Six splicers' helpers to mud-in my grave,
Take me to Kline, the Great White Father,
And let Him mourn over His gallant young slave."

112

❖ *This song is sung by Glen "Doc" Roberts, an Idaho cattle and sheep man. He learned it in about 1935*   *from his uncles, Art and Cleve, in Annabella, Utah, but Glen has lived in Idaho all of his life.* —R.S.

SHEEPHERDER'S SONG

As Sung by Glen Roberts

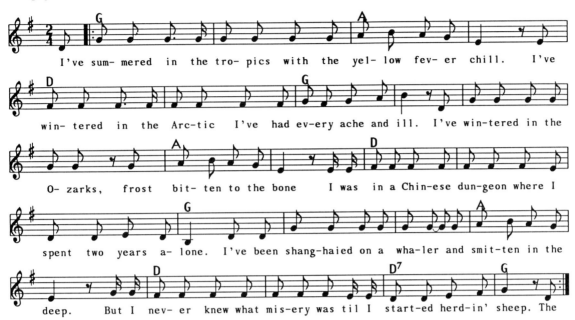

I've summered in the tropics with the yellow fevered chill,
I have wintered in the Ozarks, I've had every ache and ill
I've wintered in the arctic, frost bitten to the bone
I was in a Chinese dungeon where I spent two years alone.
I've been shanghaied on a whaler, I've been smitten in the deep,
But I didn't know what misery was till I started herdin' sheep.

The camp boss now is two months late and the burro's dead three days.
The dogs are all sore footed but them sheep they've got to graze.
They won't bed down till after dark and they're gone before the dawn.
They're bleatin' and they're blattin'. They're scattered and they're gone.
I smell their wooley stink all night and I hear them in my sleep.
I didn't know what misery was till I started herdin' sheep.

It's nice to tell the kids of the big old horny ram
Of that soft-eyed mother ewe, and that wooly little lamb.
It's nice to have your mutton chops and your woolen clothes to wear,
But did you ever give a thought to the guy that put them there?
Old Job had lots of patience but he got off plenty cheap.
He didn't know what misery was 'cause he never did herd sheep.

John Sheehy and I wrote "The Gun from Idaho" one night in 1985 (with the help of some cold beer). We sang it at the Union County Fair as a part of John's sheep shearing demonstration. The song itself is a folk adaptation of the traditional and widely-known Australian shearing ballad, "Flash Jack from Gundagai," in which a shearer tells of his experiences as an itinerant shearer in Australia. In traditional folk style, *we have kept the tune and the basic poem of the Australian ballad, but regionalized the places, language, and events to the American northwest, where John Sheehy has been shearing professionally for fifteen years. This version expresses the experience of northwestern shearers and recognizes the need to dignify and celebrate their hard and colorful lives in their own language.*

— George Venn
La Grande, Oregon

AN INTERVIEW WITH THE GUN FROM IDAHO

George Venn: John, when would you sing this song and who would you sing this for?

John Sheehy: Well, the one time that I do remember singing it, the most enjoyable time, was out at Dogcreek Well, which is near Montella, Nevada, about 60 miles, and it had been a long, hot, dry spell. We had been shearing for three weeks and everyone was tired and so you try to forget about work during, you know, in the evening. It was good weather for a change and so we had the campfire and we were all sitting around the fire, telling stories. And then the sheepman came over with his guitar and his wife and they sang some songs for us. He passed the guitar on and everybody had a try at it that wanted to, and it came to my turn and I sang the song that George and I had written two or three years before that and everybody loved it. They thought it was great. I had several copies of the song, and they all disappeared that night.

George: I notice that we talk in the song about old man Fairchild. Is that a reference to a real person, John? Is that somebody you worked for?"

John: Sure is! In fact, I was shearing for that guy then. We were in Nevada shearing.

George: Where does this man live in Idaho? Old man Fairchild.

John: Ya, he's from Buhl, Idaho. He's been shearing for over forty years.

George: Did you tell me once that your dad sheared for him, too?

John: Yes, my dad sheared for him.

George: What kind of person is he to work for?

John: He's a tough man. He's the kind of guy that you love. He demands loyalty and respect and gets it. Or, he doesn't get anything and for that reason he has a certain type of guy that works for him. He sort of 'weeds out' the trouble makers. It's a good outfit.

George: Now I know the title of our song means something to you and me because you explained to me what it means. When somebody is hearing this song and they hear the 'Gun From Idaho,' what does the 'Gun' mean, John? It isn't a reference to a pistol, right?

John: No, it's not a reference to a pistol, but it means exactly the same thing as a gunfighter, except, we work with sheep. Our tally is what wins us the fight. So, a 'Gun' is a guy that shears the most sheep.

George: What's the guy called, John, who shears the least number of sheep?

John: Ya, that's the 'Stone Popper'.

George: And we don't talk about the 'Stone Popper'?

John: No. No, anybody that's packing the rock isn't popular. No, that's not really true. It's the 'Gun' that captures the essence of the job that we have, I guess you could say.

George: Now, how long have you been shearing in the Intermountain West, John?

John: I started in 1971. That was my first year with Fairchild, and I've been around other places since then. I'm shearing for him now, though.

George: Who did you learn from, John?

John: Well, my dad started me. I think most shearers learn from their dads, or their family. It's that kind of a job. It goes from generation to generation. At least it seems to. There's an amazing number of guys whose fathers were shearers before them.

114

Sheep shearing. (Photo courtesy of Idaho Commission on the Arts)

George: Is there anything else we should let Rosalie in on here? Or anyone that is listening to this? It's an 'after work' kind of song.

John: Ya, it tells a story. Every name mentioned in this is a place where shearers go. Some of them are on the map, some of them are white spots on the map that shearers know about that means something to them, but no one else, but maybe a few sheepherders.

George: How do shearers get along with sheepherders, John?

John: Well, they're a different class of people. I'm not saying that anyone is better than the other, you take them as individuals. A sheepherder would probably tend to be more philosophical, a guy that can be on his own. Where shearers are mostly sociable-type people. They run to town when they get the chance, they work as hard as they can, and they play as hard as they can.

George: In this last stanza, there is a guy coming back from town. What's he been doing in town there, John? Would you guess?

John: Well, what I would guess he's been doing, having been shearing for almost twenty years, I bet he's been out on-the-town a little bit. It's a pretty common occurrence. Maybe in the last part of the season, the guy has been working real hard. We go to Wyoming after a hard run in Utah, which is pretty hard work because the weather is dry. We come out of Idaho into Utah, then up to Wyoming. When we get to Wyoming, that means we're almost done with our season and we start relaxing a bit. So, the Stockmans is a place in a town in Wyoming where shearers gather.

George: They go there and drink Pepsi do they?

John: No, we go there and drink beer. Some guys drink Pepsi. That's all right! That guy at the Stockmans will cash a check from anywhere.

115

GUN FROM IDAHO

Written by John Sheehy and George Venn

CHORUS: All among the wool, boys, all among the wool
Keep your comb full, boys, keep your comb full
I can shear a pretty high tally myself whenever I have a go
They know me 'round the country as "The Gun From Idaho."

VERSES: I've shorn at Wah Wah Valley and up to Jericho
I've shorn along the Big Wood for a mighty tough Basco
But before the shearing was over, I wished I was on the go
A shearing for Old Man Fairchild in Southern Idaho.

I've pinked them with a J.B., I've raced with a Special too
I've shaved them in the grease, boys, hayseeds showing through
But I never cobbed at all, boys, I never missed a blow
When shearing for Old Man Fairchild in Southern Idaho.

I've shorned on the Umatilla and on Wind River too
And once I camped for forty days at famous Jericho
At Salt Flats and Butter Creek, as far as Jackson Hole
But I was always glad to get back again to Southern Idaho.

I've made it to the Stockmans through a couple feet a snow
Got back just at sunup in time to grind my tools
When Gabriel blows his trumpet, boys, I'll pack my camp and go
A shearing for Old Man Fairchild in Southern Idaho.

❖ *George Venn collected this song and the following notes from Mrs. Margaret Christian, Wallace, Idaho, in April, 1977. Ghigleri was Guy Ghigleri, a local character who ran a limousine-styled bus in the Coeur d'Alene Mining District in north Idaho in the early part of the century. "Woe be the person who got in his way or tried to pass him," said Mrs. Christian. —R.S.*

GHIGLERI'S CANNONBALL
(Sung To the Tune of
"The Wabash Cannonball")

From the banks of the Coeur d'Alene River
To the mighty Glidden shore
From the downtown streets of Wallace
To Otto Olson's store

There's a bus of majestic splendor
That's known quite well by all —
It's the modern accommodation
Called Ghigleri's Cannonball.

Great cities of importance
We meet along our way —
There's Woodland Park and Gem Town
And Frisco by the way;

There's Black Bear and Yellow Dog
And Burke above them all —
You reach them by no other
Than Ghigleri's Cannonball.

She pulled right into Gem Town
On a cold December day.
As she pulled into the station
You could hear the people say:

There's a Wop from the Dago Queen
He's long and he's tall.
He just came up from the late shift
On Ghigleri's Cannonball.

Now here's to Guy Ghigleri
May his name forever stand
To be honored and respected
By muckers through the land;

When his earthly days are over
And the angels to him call,
They'll carry him up Nine Mile
In Jack Bever's cannonball.

Now here's to old Jack Bever
He owns the big black ship.
It's strictly a one-way ticket, boys.
He has you on his hip.

When his earthly days are over
And the curtains round him fall
They'll carry him up Nine Mile
In his own black cannonball.

"Ghigleri's Cannonball" in Burke Canyon.(Photo courtesy of Jan Boles)

❖ *Mrs. Stella Hendren had this in her 100,000 song collection — a humdinger of an Idaho trucker's song — looks to me like it should be sung to the tune of Casey Jones.* —R.S.

IDAHO RED
(to the tune of "Casey Jones")

Listen to the story of a trav'lin man,
He has a reputation all across the land
With a Frue-hauf special on a G.M.C.
He can haul a bigger load than the Robert E. Lee!

He takes a load of oranges from the Frisco dock
And gets to Sacramento after five o'clock,
The motor starts to hummin', "Donners Pass or bust!"
Then he shags it out for Denver in a cloud of dust.
He hits Reno, Lovelock, Winnemuca, Battle Mountain,
Elko, Wells, and Salt Lake, too;
He tows a burned out flivver into Steamboat Springs,
And he sets her down in Denver when the curfew rings!

Idaho red, wheelin' and a-dealin',
Idaho red, watch him reel and rock!
A highway forty main line driver
With a gal at ev'ry coffee stop!

He has a little session with the boys at cards,
Then gets a load of cattle at the Denver yards;
He heads for Kansas City and for old "Saint Louis"
'Cause he has a little date with a gal in ol'Missou!
He hits Limon, Russel, Salina, Junction City,
Manhattan, Topeka and ol'K.C.
At Booneville and Columbia he's rollin' great
And he makes the Mississippi at a quarter eight!

He goes to Indianapolis for a brand new load,
He checks her at Columbus, then he hits the road
For old Atlantic City on the Eastern shore,
But he's bound to stay a little while in Baltimore!
He hits Jamesville, Cambridge, Wheelering, Uniontown,
Cumberland, Hagerstown and Frederick too;
When he gets to Wilmington he's feelin' fine,
'Cause he knows Atlantic City is the end of the line!

Gill School north of Emmett, 1902.(Photo courtesy of Idaho State Historical Society)

❖ *I found this poem in Snake River Echoes published by the Upper Snake River Historical Society in 1982. I included this piece because it is one of the few verses I could locate about an occupation dominated by women. I'd be interested to know about any other occupational songs by women that are out there.*

—R.S.

I STILL TEACH SCHOOL

I write no poem, men's hearts to thrill.
No song to sing to light men's souls;
To battles front, no soldiers lead,
In halls of state, I boast no skills;
   I just teach school.

And they my students, game intent
On cherished thoughts they soon shall reach,
And mine, the hands that led them on!
And I inspired — there content.
And even now, I still teach school!

(t. left) John Atkinson's Blacksmith Shop, Boise. (Photo courtesy of Idaho State Historical Society)

(t. right) Sheepherder, southern Idaho. (Photo courtesy of Idaho State Historical Society)

(center) Ben and Raymond Crisp, logging.(Photo courtesy of Bonner County Historical Society)

Cattle drive (Photo courtesy of Idaho State Historical Society)

This poem is based on a true story about a petty thief who was apprehended and tried in the saloon at Rocky Bar station. The hanging fizzled and the man was released. The poem was printed in "Incredible Idaho," October 1969, with a picture of the old Rock Creek stage station. It appears to have been submitted as "Rock Creek Reports," by Charlotte Crockett (date unknown), and it sets the location of the action as the old Stricker Saloon. I believe the column, which was sent to me by Sudie Stuart Hagen, was from a Twin Falls newspaper.
        —Helen Olsen
        Wilder

BALLAD OF THE SWAMPER
(Prisoner at the Bar)

A dust-stained swamper came one day
To the store at Rock Creek Station,
Looking for a few days' work
And a little conversation.

He carried water, cut up wood,
And added to his kitty
Until he thought he had enough
To leave for Boise City.

But one mistake this swamper made:
He paused at the barroom door,
Went inside, and tossed his sack
Of baggage on the floor.

It landed with a clatter,
An odd metallic sound;
And every man along the bar
Looked curiously around.

"Leaving us?" the barkeep asked.
"Yep — guess I'll hit the road."
"That sack sounds heavy," someone said,
"For such a small-sized load."

"What's in it?" And they turned it out,
And there upon the floor
Were several cans of milk and jam
He'd stolen from the store.

"A dirty thief!" and "Grab him, boys!"
The angry mutters grew.
The swamper eyed them nervously
And sipped his mountain dew.

"Let's string him up!" "Who's got a rope?"
"Hold on!" the barkeep yelled.
"This man's entitled to a trial.
I aim to see one held!"

They chose up judge and jury
In less than half a wink;
And then the prisoner and court
All had another drink.

The agent was to prosecute,
The barkeep to defend.
The judge gave his instructions,
Not hard to comprehend:

"If guilty, he'll be doomed to hang.
If innocent he's found,
He'll be assessed the costs of court,
To-wit, drinks all around."

Though they were tempted to acquit,
They overcame the pang.
They pondered, found him guilty,
And sentenced him to hang.

They tossed a rope across a beam,
And dangled it in air;
They put a noose around his neck,
And someone brought a chair.

As all hands grasped the tightened rope,
The barkeep's voice was heard:
"Hold on! This prisoner has a right
To say a final word."

Then the pilgrim spoke up grimly,
"To a better world. Here goes!"
He leaped in space and thrashed about,
Reaching with his toes.

Startled by this sudden turn,
The hangmen lost their hold.
The swamper dropped down on the floor
And lay there, stretched out cold.

"See what you've done!" the barkeep yelled.
"He only stole some grub.
A man must eat, though he may be
The lowest kind of scrub!"

We hung him once," the judge decreed.
"It's only common sense
You can't hang any man but once,
At least for the same offense."

So they poured some brandy down him,
And added to his pack,
And sent him off with a lusty cheer.
I don't think he ever went back.

121

Maidell Clemets sent "When the Mill Went Up the Spout" to the Wallace concert. When I finally tracked him down I found a man who is steeped in the history of the hard-rock, hard-sociable country around Wallace and Kellogg.

He has ledgers full of fascinating stories of the old days in that part of Idaho carefully hand-written and well-told.

I hope someday soon these memories will be published.

(Photo courtesy of Michael Cordell)

COME ALL YE TOILING MILLIONS

SONGS AND STORIES OF STRUGGLE

Come, all ye toiling millions that labor for your life
To support yourselves and families, your children and
*   your wife;*
Come, rally to our standard now in this gigantic strife,
Then we'll go marching to victory.

Hannibal F. Johnson

As long as poor people and working people have been oppressed by the rich and powerful, there have been protest songs.

Linking arms or hands and letting common needs and resolves flow through our bodies, hearts, and minds while singing a common song is one of the most potent means of gaining the power to banish fear and accomplish what seemed impossible. Witness how the protestors in Soweto, unarmed but undaunted, sing in the path of bullets and violence; hear the oppressed of Central and South America sing Violetta Para's "Gracias a La Vida" (Thanks to Life) almost as an anthem; and listen to civil rights freedom fighters chanting, "We Shall Overcome" and "Carry It On." The spirit of these songs extends all the way back to our own revolution, to the French Revolution, and as far back as there is memory. The Intermountain West has also produced some powerful songs for change. The title song in this section was written by Hannibal F. Johnson and published in Poems of Idaho (1895).

—R.S.

("Silent agitator" stickers courtesy of Industrial Workers of the World)

123

COME ALL YE TOILING MILLIONS

Written by Hannibal F. Johnson

Come, all ye toiling millions that labor for your life
To support yourselves and families, your children and
    your wife;
Come, rally to our standard now in this gigantic strife,
    Then we'll go marching to victory.

CHORUS:
Hurrah! Hurrah! Our banner is unfurled.
Hurrah! Hurrah! It's waving proudly o'er the world.
The tyrants and the robbers from their places will be hurled
As we go marching to victory.

Come, join the brave Alliance, boys, and help the
    cause along;
Our battle is for freedom now, against a giant wrong.
We never will give up our homes to such a thieving throng,
    As we go marching to victory.

We're fighting old monopoly and the gigantic trust.
They've taken all the corn and oil, left us the cob and husk;
But when we get our ballots in, you'll hear their
    bubble burst.
    As we go marching to victory.

Labor solidarity continues as seen in this solidarity march in Lewiston, September 3, 1990. (Photograph by Barry Kough, courtesy of Lewiston Morning Tribune.*)*

The promises they made us, not one was ever kept;
But 'round the tree of liberty the sneaking tyrants crept.
They sought to blight our heritage while quietly we slept,
 But we'll go marching to victory.

They gobbled up our greenbacks then issued out their bond;
Then made us pay the interest to support the thieving throng.
And when we made objection, they told us we were wrong,
 But we'll go marching to victory.

They've taken all our land estate and claim it as their own,
While husbands, wives, and children are left without a home;
And willing hands to foreign lands in search of work
  must roam,
 But we'll go marching to victory.

The bankers rob the farmers, and the railroads steal
  the land,
And in their cursed robbing schemes, they both go hand
  in hand.
They think our business is to obey while theirs is
  to command,
 But we'll go marching to victory.

We've trusted the Republicans and failed to take a trick;
We've leaned upon the Democrats and found a broken stick;
We'll try the Knights and Farmers now and then you'll see
  how quick
 That we'll go marching to victory.

And now we stand united, the bosses best look out;
With faith and honor plighted, we'll put them all to rout.
And with an honest ballot now we'll put the rascals out
 As we go marching to victory.

❖ *We collected "Fifty-Thousand Lumberjacks" from Mrs. Howard (Leila) Olin of St. Maries who was celebrating her ninetieth birthday the day we visited her. As a correspondent for* The Spokane Chronicle, *she wrote an article in 1970 about logging in the St. Maries area in the early 1900's. In the article (reprinted below), she quotes Eli Laird, a steamboat captain who worked on the St. Joe River and Lake Coeur d'Alene for thirty years.* —R.S.

50,000 LUMBERJACKS
by Leila Olin

Logging camps were crude shelters in the early days. Bunkhouses accommodating about 40 men had no floors in them and the bunks were placed one above the other with hay mattresses.

Describing the camp, Laird wrote: "It looked like a pile of cordwood when all the heads were lying in a row the full length of the building. They had two big heating stoves but no ventilation whatever. The men hung their shirts, socks and mackinaws on pegs near the roof. When they got up full steam in there with maybe 100 men chewing tobacco and smoking, it became a place a coyote could have smelled miles over the hills."

Men carried their home on their backs in sougans which always contained their bedrolls. They were furnished with five gallon cans in which to bathe and "boil up" or wash their clothes. Conditions improved in the camps where the Industrial Workers of the World came in 1914. About 200 IWW members or wobblies came from Seattle, Portland, Spokane and Butte, Mont., established a tent camp at the mouth of Marble Creek on the St. Joe River. They began an organizational drive and succeeded. The loggers struck, stopping all operations.

During the drive, about 100 Wobblies lined up on each side of the trail forcing loggers to run the gauntlet. The rough men of the woods were so intimidated that many joined the organization.

According to Harold Wayne, Spokane, strike breakers hired by the lumber companies arrived in thin clothing and Oxford shoes to go on the drive to Marble Creek. Three days of that rugged labor was more than they could stand.

One of the favorite songs of the time sung to the tune of "Portland County Jail" was

50,000 Lumberjacks, 50,000 packs,

50,000 dirty rolls of blankets on their backs.

50,000 minds made up to strike and strike like men.

For 50 years they've packed a bed, but never will again.

As a result of the strike, tin plates and straw beds were thrown out the window. Improvements such as sheets, screens, shorter hours and better food became standard fare.

FIFTY THOUSAND LUMBERJACKS

As Sung by Leila Olin   (*Sung to the tune of "Portland County Jail"*)

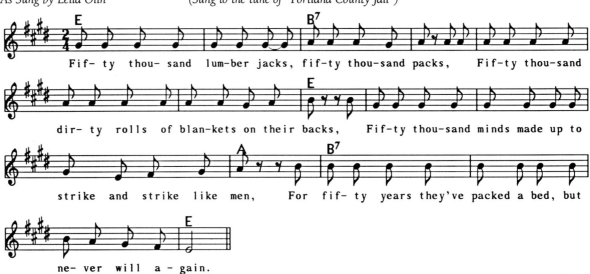

Fif-ty thou-sand lum-ber jacks, fif-ty thou-sand packs, Fif-ty thou-sand dir-ty rolls of blan-kets on their backs, Fif-ty thou-sand minds made up to strike and strike like men, For fif-ty years they've packed a bed, but ne-ver will a-gain.

Fifty thousand lumberjacks, fifty thousand packs,
Fifty thousand dirty rolls of blankets on their backs.
Fifty thousand minds made up to strike and strike like men;
For fifty years they've "packed" a bed, but never
    will again.

CHORUS:
"Such a lot of devils"—that's what the papers say—
"They've gone on strike for shorter hours and some increase
    in pay.
They left the camps, the lazy tramps, they all walked out
    as one;
They say they'll win the strike or put the bosses on
    the bum."

Fifty thousand wooden bunks full of things that crawl;
Fifty thousand restless men have left them once for all.
One by one they dared not say, "Fat, the hours are long."
If they did they'd hike—but now they're fifty
    thousand strong.

Fatty Rich, we know your game, know your pride is pricked.
Say—but why not be a man, and own when you are licked?
They've joined the One Big Union—gee—for goodness sake,
    get wise!
The more you try to buck them now, the more they organize.

Take a tip and start right in—plan some cozy rooms
Six or eight spring beds in each, with towels, sheets
    and brooms;
Shower baths for men who work keep them well and fit;
A laundry, too, and drying room, would help a little bit.

Get some dishes, white and clean; good pure food to eat;
See that cook has help enough to keep the table neat.
Tap the bell for eight hours' work; treat the boys
    like men,
And fifty thousand lumberjacks may come to work again.

Men who work should be well paid—"A man's a man
    for a' that."
Many a man has a home to keep same as yourself, Old Fat.
Mothers, sisters, sweethearts, wives, children, too, galore
Stand behind the men to win this bread and butter war.

❖ *T-Bone Slim, who wrote "The Lumberjack's Prayer," had his "Answer to the Prayer" printed on small colored cards which he sold to raise money for the International Workers of the World (I.W.W.). His real name was Matt Valentine Hruhta, and in addition to circulating his own songs and those of Joe Hill, he was a labor organizer in the Northwest and spent some time with Aunt Molly Jackson. He finished his life as a tug-boat captain on the Hudson River barge, "The Casey." T-Bone Slim died in 1942, the old Wobblies say, like the Chinese poet Li Po—drunk—trying to embrace the moon in the water.*

I got this song from Bert Russel's book, Swiftwater People *(1979), in which Bert describes having met T-Bone Slim. The song is still sung around the Northwest. Utah Phillips renders it with great gusto.*—R.S.

THE LUMBERJACK'S PRAYER
(To the Tune of "The Old Hundred")
By T-Bone Slim

I'll pray dear Lord for Jesus sake.
Give us this day a T-bone steak.
Hallowed be Thy holy name
But don't forget to send the same.

Hear my humble cry, Oh Lord!
And send me down some decent board:
Brown gravy on some German fried
And sliced tomatoes on the side.

Observe me on my bended legs
I'm askin' you for ham and eggs
And of the hottest custard pies
I like, Dear Lord, the largest size.

Oh! Hear my cry Almighty Host
I quite forgot the quail on toast.
Let Thy kindly heart be stirred
And spread some oysters on that bird.

Dear Lord, we know Thy holy wish
On Friday we must have a fish.
Our flesh is weak, our spirits stale
You'd better make that fish a whale.

Oh, Hear me Lord! Remove those dogs
The sausages of powdered logs
The bull beef hash and bearded snouts
Take them to hell or thereabouts.

With alum bread and pressed beef butts
Dear Lord! You damn near ruined my guts.
Your whitewash milk and Oleorine
I wish to Christ I'd never seen.

O, Hear me Lord! I'm praying still
But if you won't, our union will
Put porkchops on the bill of fare
And starve no workers anywhere.

Bull Pen, Kellogg: 1899. (Barnard Stockbridge Collection. University of Idaho Library.)

ANSWER TO THE PRAYER

I am happy to say this prayer has been answered — by the "old man" himself. He tells me He has furnished — plenty for all — and that if I am not getting mine it's because I am not organized SUFFICIENTLY strong to force the master to loosen up. He tells me he has no knowledge of Dogs, Pressed-Beef Butts, etc., and that they probably are products of the Devil. He further informs me the Capitalists are children of His — and that He absolutely refuses to participate in any children's squabbles. He believes in letting us fight it out along the lines of Industrial Unionism.

Yours in faith,
T-Bone Slim

Note: The money derived from the sale of these, goes for the payment of putting out free literature.

Let me point out once more, in my gentle way, the depression of this country is not political and a billion politicians one or all working ain't gonna cure it; the running of a bunch of patriots ain't gonna cure it; the running of a bunch of christians ain't gonna cure it; the running of a bunch of convicts, combines or cleopatras ain't gonna cure it. These have little more effect on a trouble that is economic than has a row of brass monkeys.

To cure depression, you must join a good labor union, preferably the I.W.W.—whatever union you choose, it must be its composition—or no cure. If you do not join a labor union you thereby go on record as being well pleased with the depression. And I hope you will continue to like it.

Life in a political arena is a precise reflex of the gigantic economic struggle as between banks and plants, going on, at this moment, in this country. Plants take a wallop at the banks and Brookhart goes spinning like a headless rooster in a cornfield. Banks haul off with an upper cut and Massachusetts goes wet. Plants land a long swing to the snout and Mooney stays in the can. Banks put in a low punch and Kresel shows signs of being an angel of high emprise. Plants rock banks' head with a terrific left to the jaw and Britt Smith, Centralia Boys, stay in Walla Walla, and so on.

Interference in this struggle by an outsider shall cause Banks and Plants to turn on the intruder.

Coolidge said we've got lots of prosperity, have some soup.

Harding before him said take the teapot, we got lots of it.

Hoover said, we've got lots of it and declared in favor of a moratorium just as Europe was about to pay its debts. We've got lots of it—last week in New York City I didn't get one single meal. What I got was as follows:

—Forty-one cups of coffee (frail stuff).

—Sixty-two rolls of all description and some of no description at all.

—Eighty-three slices of bread and sixty cubes of grease.

—About one bathtubful of soup.

—One mushmelon, eight bananas—all of 'em rotten.

Note: I didn't try to influence the city either one

way or another—this diet is her voluntary contribution to science. It never occurs to N.Y.C. that Germans and Finns have thrived since time immemorial on full meals and that an occasional bellyful couldn't hurt a guy even if he is unemployed. Nay brother, political action is no action—it is a result.

For me to say, farmers or store keepers can remedy this depression by organizing farmer or store keeper union is to say a falsehood—they can not. They are not numerous enough and they are not on the ground floor.

They are merely the flora in the potato patch—labor is the big baked potato. Labor is the only power in this world that can cure this depression—and cure it to stay cured. This it can do only by organizing a one big union of the workers and by declining all help from parasites or their representatives.

The minute it gets any help from bosses of any shade or description the bets are all off—and the depression shall have a relapse. Labor or Oblivion!

P.S.—The fight between Banks and Plants is for to determine which shall be permitted to skin labor—a senseless, insane struggle.—Soup versus Worms: Do not think me unduly prejudiced against soup. Soup is all right in its place. I can conceive of nothing more suitable for fish to swim in—a combination of sport and nourishment, barbless breakfast you might say. And in re N.Y.C.'s soupability, let me say, I could have changed that at any time by lying a little, tell Mr. Knickerbocker that the soup-shower occurred the week before. He would have risen to the occasion promptly—but a test is a test. As in buying a pair of sox I fell one penny short of the price: Knickerbocker howled loud and long that he must not be driven to the wailing wall, he must get his full ten cents.

"Now lookit here, Knick," says I dropping the pennies into my pocket, "I'm a poor man whose family passed off by starvation.—Why not make it a gift of a pair of sox so I can cover my nakedness?" "I'll tell you what I'll do," says Knick, "I'll give you that pair of sox for nine cents."

You see, Knick stood to lose sox or gain nine cents—he chose the nine—business is business.

Soup we will have even in the workers' commonwealth, and the parasites shall eat it.

As we approach the seventy-fifth anniversary of his execution by a Utah firing squad, it is important to acknowledge the legacies of Joe Hill. In addition to providing us with labor anthems like "There is Power in a Union," and the classic I.W.W. song, "The *Preacher and the Slave," Joe Hill's life (and death) remind us all of the importance of personal conviction which leads to collective action. As he himself said, "Don't mourn, organize!"* —Robert McCarl

THE PREACHER AND THE SLAVE
Written by Joe Hill

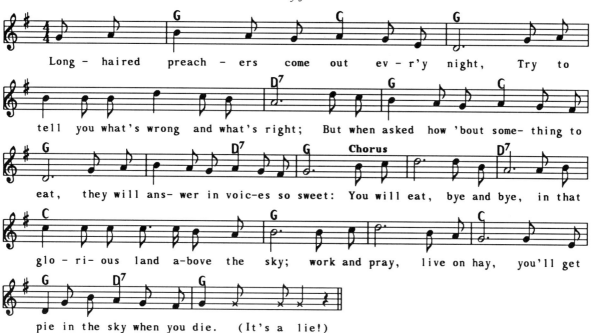

Long - haired preach - ers come out ev - r'y night, Try to tell you what's wrong and what's right; But when asked how 'bout some- thing to eat, they will ans- wer in voic-es so sweet: You will eat, bye and bye, in that glo - ri- ous land a-bove the sky; work and pray, live on hay, you'll get pie in the sky when you die. (It's a lie!)

Long haired preachers come out every night.
Try to tell you what's wrong and what's right.
But when asked how 'bout something to eat
They will answer with voices so sweet:

CHORUS:
You will eat, bye and bye,
In that glorious land above the sky.
Work and pray! Live on hay!
You'll get pie in the sky when you die.

2nd Verse:
And the Starvation Army they play
And they sing and they clap and they pray,
Till they get all your coin on the drum,
Then they tell you when you're on the bum:

CHORUS:
You will eat, bye and bye,
In that glorious land above the sky.
Work and pray! Live on Hay!
You'll get pie in the sky when you die.
(All together, shouted) IT'S A LIE!

THE SECOND BATTLE OF BUNKER HILL
By Maidell Clemets

The Huttons bought another thirty-second share of the Hercules mine for $375.00. Harry Orchard's bluff at stability failed quickly when he lost his share gambling. He went to work in the Tiger-Poorman Mine and joined the Western Federation of Miners, a casual move that would chart a violent course ending in forty-eight years behind bars. Day, a bookkeeper and business manager for the mine, increased his holdings. Damien Cardoner, a Portuguese grocer, bought in along with the Markwells, former employers of Orchard and Paulsen. All believed in the Hercules. They spent their spare time and money on it. When May wasn't cooking (perhaps for Arment's new hotel) she was mucking out the mine or creating stews and roasts for the crew. Times got discouraging. The Hercules prospects began to be referred to as the "suspect." Gus Paulsen might turn up at the Huttons' door after a week's work with a sample bag that held less than a few gleams of hope. May cooked up big dinners, and encouraged the clan with rich words and fine food.

Always ready to stab a thick finger in one more pie, May Hutton got her chance during "The Second Battle of Bunker Hill." Radical union men had dominated the seven years since the "Troubles of '92" with a reign of terror. A Congressional committee would later describe the scene in the Coeur d'Alenes as "The most flagrant lawlessness that stains the pages of American history." May held labor meetings in her house regularly. It's doubtful that May sanctioned the violent methods of the union leaders, but to her the Cause justified the means. It was a time of "anarchy and insurrection" in the words of the investigating Congressional committee in 1900. May's old friend, Edward Boyce, now President of the Western Federation of Miners, arrived in Wallace in April, 1899, to confront the Bunker Hill and Sullivan. He had built the Federation into the most powerful labor group in the West by insisting on high wages and a closed shop. The managers of the Coeur d'Alene Union Mines had called on him to force the Bunker Hill and Sullivan to raise its wages, or else let them lower their own pay scale accordingly. Bunker Hill had held out against the union, using company spotters to finger union infiltrators. When confronted by Boyce, the superintendent agreed to hike the pay; and then

fired seventeen miners found to be union men — a deliberate spit in the face. As a result, several hundred Bunker Hill and Sullivan employees "quit" because union men seized the tramway that carried them to work. War was at hand.

On April 29, 1899, the miners reported to the union halls instead of to work. They were informed that the officers of the union had decided to blow up the Bunker Hill and Sullivan. The union voted by a slim margin to go ahead with the plan. They scattered to their homes, tied with white arm bands, grabbed their guns and regrouped at the Burke depot. Revolver in hand, Harry Orchard joined the crowd waiting for Al Hutton to bring the train up from Wallace. The whistle blew, and the train pulled in. Eight masked, armed men got on board and ordered the crew to add six boxcars. When everyone had climbed aboard, a ringleader shoved a gun in Al's ribs and told him to stop at the Frisco powder house. Volunteers broke open the doors and loaded forty boxes of dynamite and a supply of caps. Next stop, Gem Union Hall, where they loaded a hidden cache of arms, ammunition, and 200 more men. Someone decided that they didn't have enough dynamite for total destruction, so Al backed up to the Frisco where they took on fifty more pounds. A lone horseman galloped ahead of the train down to Wallace, wheeled in front of the Federation's official newspaper office, and shouted, "They are coming!"

A huge crowd had massed at the Wallace depot, lining the tracks, when Al slowed the train. The Mullan union members, 600 strong, were armed and ready to jump aboard. The sheriff and his deputy, both union supporters, joined the train. Miners scrambled on top of the boxcars as Al balked at heading down a foreign line, for the rails from Wallace to Wardner were owned by Oregon Railway and Navigation Company, not Union Pacific. He couldn't even warn ahead to oncoming trains because the union officers had taken the precaution of cutting all the telegraph wires. But he felt a Winchester 45-90 at his back so he pulled the throttle and started the "mixed special" — twelve hundred delighted terrorists and forty-five hundred pounds of dynamite. The crowd roared cheers and the men dangling from the cars yelled back, singing the train to Wardner to the tune of

"There'll be a Hot Time in the Old Town Tonight."

The Dynamite Express whistled, cautioned around curves, and over trestles. Harry Orchard recalled:

> It all seemed like a gigantic picnic . . . . I doubt that many of us that day thought we were breaking the law by stealing a train and forcing its crew to run us where we wanted to go regardless of other trains . . . . Everybody was joking.

At Wardner the men formed two lines in good order. The Sheriff burlesqued a command to disperse. Even those who could barely speak English laughed at the mockery. Rifled men led the attack, followed by those with side arms. A contingent had gone up ahead to draw the guards' attention. This advance guard fired a shot, signalling the army to come ahead, for only sixty armed scabs were seen, and they were fleeing for the mountains. But the mass of men thought the shot was from a guard and some hotheads started firing at their own advance men, killing one. A detachment including Harry Orchard shouldered the ninety cases of dynamite and headed up the hill. Gem Union leader Davis ordered the placement of the charges. Orchard, fascinated with the science of dynamite, was the first to step forward as a volunteer to set off the charges. After lighting the fuses the dynamite men narrowly escaped out a window as three blasts rocked the hills for twenty miles and sent the concentrator—one of the largest in North America—up in a volcano of wood, smoke, and fire. "From the force of the third shot, debris was hurled in every direction, and a huge canopy was formed in the heavens. Fragments of machinery and broken timbers rained down upon the ruins for several seconds," reported the enthusiastic editor of the *Idaho State Tribune*, James Sovereign. "The work was planned and executed by men who have received the training of a life time in the handling of dynamite."

It was a glorious sight, inspiring the men to set fire to the boarding house, the elegant home of the superintendent, and finally the town of Wardner. Davis had Al blow a few whistle blasts. By this time a lot of whiskey had been washed down, and on the way home the men on the boxcars made a target of the flume on the hillside above the train, cheering as water spurted in fountains from the bullet holes.

Davis admonished them to save their ammunition; Federal troops were on their way. Back in Wallace, families were evacuating to Spokane, the depot crowded with a mob of frightened, crying women and children. One man was dead, another dying, and the Sheriff wired the Governor: PEACEFUL NIGHT STOP EVERYTHING UNDER CONTROL. But as Orchard mused: "It occurred to me that, after all, you can't steal railroad trains, dynamite mines, and burn villages without some reaction."

Hiding out on forested mountainsides, Orchard and the Union leaders watched soldiers swarm off a train, "round up the miners like a bunch of cattle and herd them into boxcars." In Butte, Edward Boyce told Orchard that the Bunker Hill and Sullivan management was solely responsible for the riots:

> The same miners would have waded in blood to their knees if necessary, to protect the property of the Mullan or Burke Canyon operators. Bunker Hill did everything to aggravate union men.

Under orders from the War Department, Brigadier General H. C. Merriam had brought in 700 soldiers. They arrested 200 men and stuffed them in a Wardner hay barn. It was so crowded that they had to shift to boxcars while carpenters threw up barracks in barbed wire fences— the bullpens in Wardner and Wallace. One local headline announced "Army Arrests Every Male in Burke." At one point 700 prisoners were packed in the pens without sanitary facilities or bedding. The outraged labor press called it "the most flagrant violation of the rights of *habeas corpus* ever known in the United States." To get out and go back to work, the miners had to sign a statement denying their participation in the uprising, giving up any union membership for life, and agreeing that the crimes committed were directed by the miners' union. Sheriff Young was impeached and replaced by the Bunker Hill and Sullivan's company doctor, Hugh France. Federal Negro troops ransacked houses in search of arms and subjected the prisoners to harassment with the encouragement of the white officers. When an escape tunnel was discovered (a digger had poked a ventilation hole through the surface and jabbed a sleeping guard in the back), the prisoners were put on bread and water for eight days for refusing to fill up the tunnel.

❖ *Maidell Clemets of Osburn tells us this song is a sequel to the famous "Bull Pen Song." He says, "Arthur Sargent, a mining engineer who died several years ago, gave me the original song; his father came to Murray in 1884. He was a blacksmith and, at one time, was reported to be the strongest man in the Coeur d'Alenes. The family had a farm on Two Mile Creek near Osburn."* —R.S.

WHEN THE MILL WENT UP THE SPOUT

(Sung to the tune of "The Wearing of the Green")   *Written by Arthur Sargent*

We are numbered off like convicts.
    Though we never broke the laws;
We stood side by side like brothers
    For labor's noble cause.
The world looks on with pitying eye,
    Yet we bravely bear our yoke;
To save our lives for our babes and wives
    And smile, though our hearts are broke.
One Edward Boyce, chief of our choice,
    Has brought this all about,
For in the April of '99 he sent us up the spout.

CHORUS
He sent us up the spout, boys,
    He sent us up the spout;
In April of '99,
    He sent us up the spout.

Two trains steamed into Wardner
    That morning clear and bright,
The boys looked so gay and war-like
    It filled me with delight.
I tied their masks,
    I stacked their guns,
I pinned their badges on;
    For I loved each honest miner
As a mother loves a son.
    "What brought you here?"
I softly asked;
    Some sadly shook their head
While some had fondly pressed my hands.
    "I know not," others said.
Some said, "Farewell,"
    Like a funeral knell.
We soon shall meet, no doubt,
    Where angels sing
On starry wings,
    As the mill flew up the spout.

Starvation stared us in the face,
    The boys were in the Pen;
Then money flowed from pole to pole
    From honest women and men.
The boys and girls, God bless them,
With hearts so le'el and true,
    Sent in their dimes and nickels
To feed both I and you.
    The labor lodges were assessed,
And men gave their donation like knights of old,
    With hearts of gold,
From every clime and nation.
    You ask Ed Boyce:
"Where is the cash?"
    He will answer back, no doubt,
"With a Penrose pill
    From the Robbers' Roost,"
And send you up the spout.

For Cochran's wife and children
    You amply do provide,
While Crawford who gave his all for ye,
    Is walled in by the raging tide
On the sea-girt rock of Albatros,
    Far from his eastern home,
Where his mother waits and wonders
    Why her boy does never come.
While the San Quentin men
    Employment seek,
In vain, I have no doubt,
For with Boyce's chums
    And saloon bums
He sent them up the spout.

I loved you like a mother
  And my lips are ever closed;
I fed, I sheltered, and lied for you
  Which everybody knows.
You left me sick on the streets of Butte
  Without a place to lay my head,
With a snow drift for to cover me
  And the gutter for my bed.
When I asked Boyce and Maher for relief
  Their answer was a fright,
But I followed Boyce to the Robbers' Roost
  And watched him there all night.
Then he sent me to the poor-house, blind,
  With many more, no doubt,
While he wined and dined
  On your hard earned cash,
And sent us up the spout.

Ed Boyce is no Napoleon
Or he'd have saved his men
  From Boise jail and Albatros,
San Quentin and the Pen.
  Like James of old, at Derry Walls,
He took an awful fright
And dropped his pants behind him
  As he ran with all his might.
And when he reached to Oldbridge town,
  Where some friends he thought to join
He saw William Camp upon the bank,
  Then he jumped into the Boyne.
Which leaves us miners in the lurch,
  Black-listed, I've no doubt,
For in July and April
  He sent us up the spout.

Frisco Mill, Gem, after explosion, 1892. (Barnard Stockbridge Collection University of Idaho Library)

❖ *I first learned this song from Olive Wooley Burt in Salt Lake City. She was the author of* American Murder Ballads and Their Stories *(Oxford University Press, 1958). Olive and I used to present a program of murder ballads together—I would sing the songs and she would tell the stories in a voice very like Ma Perkins.*

—R.S.

THE SONG OF HARRY ORCHARD

As Sung by Rosalie Sorrels

Har- ry Or- chard is in pris- on, the rea- son you all know. He killed Frank Stue- nen- berg right here in I-da- ho. He set his bomb out care- ful- ly, he did not hes- i- tate; and he blew poor Frank to King - dom Come when he tried to shut the gate.

Harry Orchard is in prison,
The reason you all know;
He killed Frank Steunenberg
Right here in Idaho.

He set his bomb out carefully,
He did not hesitate;
It blew poor Frank to Kingdom Come
When he tried to shut the gate.

Harry says he has killed others,
For them my heart it bleeds;
He should pray for God's forgiveness
For his terrible misdeeds.

Harry blamed the Wobblies,
And maybe he spoke true,
For no one on this earth can tell
What such a band will do.

The chiefs were brought from Denver,
They were shanghaied as you know;
Bill Haywood and George Pettibone
Were brought to Idyho.

Clarence Darrow stood to shield them;
The result it was so sure:
Bill Haywood and his comrades
Free men walked out the door.

Now listen, all you young men,
The lesson it is plain:
Just be prepared to pay the cost
When you set a bomb for gain.

SABOTAGE

Sabotage means to push back, pull out or break off the fangs of Capitalism
W. D. Haywood

❖ *This is "Haywire" Mac McClintock's classic hymn to the heaven where hobos and bums could rest their weary heads and get away from railroad bulls and other police types, a place where suffering would vanish and strawberry pie would be twenty feet high — Poor Man's Heaven. McClintock was an I.W.W. organizer. He is also reputed to have written "Hallelujah, I'm a Bum!" This version of his song "Big Rock Candy Mountain" came from Betty Corrigan, Challis. I've heard the song all my life from my uncles, from old time hobos, and from bums I've known and loved.*

—R.S.

THAT BIG ROCK CANDY MOUNTAIN
Written by Mac McClintock

On a sum-mer day in the month of May, A bur-ly bum came hik-ing Down a sha-dy lane through sug-ar cane, He was look-ing for his lik-ing. As he roamed a-long he sang a song of the land and milk and hon-ey, Where a bum can stay for ma-ny a day And he won't need an-y mon-ey. Oh the buz-zin' of the bees in the cig-ar-ette trees, Near the so-da wa-ter foun-tain, At the lem-on-ade springs, where the blue-bird sings, In that Big Rock Can-dy Moun-tain.

On a summer day in the month of May,
A burly bum came hiking
Down a shady lane through sugar cane;
He was looking for his liking.
As he roamed along he sang a song
Of the land of milk and honey,
Where a bum can stay for many a day
And he won't need any money.

CHORUS:
Oh (Where the) buzzin' of the bees in the
   cigarette trees,
Near the soda water fountain,
At the lemonade springs,
Where the bluebird sings,
In that Big Rock Candy Mountain.

On a run came a farmer and his son.
To the hayfields they were bounding.
Said the bum to the son, "Don't you come,
To that Big Rock Candy Mountain."

So the very next day they hiked away,
The mileposts they kept counting.
But they never arrived at the lemonade tide
In that Big Rock Candy Mountain.

There's a lake of gin, we can both jump in,
And the handouts grow in bunches.
In the new mown hay, we sleep all day
And the bars all have free lunches,
Where the mail train stops and there ain't no cops
And the folks are tender-hearted
Where you ne'er change your socks an' you never
   throw rocks
And your hair is never parted.

Jack rolled his eyes up to the skies,
And said to the bum nam'd Sandy,
'I'm weary, I'm starv'd, I want steak to carve,
Where is that gol-darn candy?
I'll hike no more for my feet are sore,
I'll never reach that fountain.
I wanta be a home guard, with a union card,
In that Big Rock Candy Mountain.'

"The Dehorn Song" is no lyric masterpiece, but it reveals facets of labor folklore. It also shows that the Wobbly could poke fun at himself; he possessed a strain of humor sadly lacking in other sections of the radical movement. The song flays the drunkard but not in the saccharine tones of a temperance tract, for behind the portrait lay the militant dehorn squad—an instrument of social control developed by outcasts consciously dedicated to rebuilding society.

—Archie Green

❖I learned this version (sung to the tune of "Oh Tannenbaum") from my Uncle Bill (William String-fellow) who now resides in Marsing but once followed work all over the West—a true boomer. —R.S.

DEHORN SONG
(Sung to the tune of "O Tannenbaum")
A wino's nose is deepest red,
The one bright spot in an empty head . . .
So come, you workers,
Let's get wise
And quit the booze
And organize.

I can't recall a job at all . . .
My eyes are dim from swilling gin . . .
And if I die this very night
'Twill surely end my lifelong fight.

(Repeat first part.)

Frisco mine, group of miners, Gem, Idaho, 1888. (Photo courtesy of Barnard-Stockbridge Collection, University of Idaho Library)

I wrote this poem, but it was never set to music. I had worked for nine years in the Armour packing plant in Nampa. Union employees had taken two wage or benefit rollbacks. More than half of the night crew had contracted brucellosis (undulant fever) from infected cattle, and as the union safety committee representative, I filed OSHA complaints that resulted in mandatory blood testing for everyone. I was also a department steward, and seemed to keep things stirred up, so I was banished to swing shift. As the union-busting closure became imminent, I wrote this.

—Jack Trueblood

PACKIN' HOUSE BLUES, 1982

Here we sit locked down in this vulgar little hole
letting blood and bein' let.
Clinging together and sinking alone.
Who runs this place? It's not me.
Maybe it goes on by itself—
on killing and bleeding and tearing out guts.
Work here forever? You think I'm nuts?
You tell me you're leaving, I know that you're lying;
we're making a living that's more like a dying.
I'll help you, wage slave, but can't you see
they own us?

Eight hours a day is a third of your life.
If you died at fifty instead of seventy-five,
what would you trade for that other third?
So take the man's money, and flip him the bird
and try to feel free in the other two thirds.
But there is no pay for the time you worry at home
about the speed of the line, or if your hands are okay,
or what about the pain in your back today?

They'll suck out your blood but they'll throw you no bone,
'cause there's no extra money for blood of your own.
We all hang together and die one by one;
at least in groups dying should be more fun,
but it's really alone—don't you feel
alone?

We're all just as guilty as the man with the gun;
clink with the shackle and slice with the knife,
you're a blood-letter now for the rest of your life.
If you forget how to fight, the other side's won,
and you're the same as the animal under the gun.

So keep your head straight 'cause your mind is your ace,
but don't play it too close to the line.
'Cause what happens if you lose when the stakes are big,
and the pigs get your mind and you wake up a pig?

Blood-letter, meat-getter, you packin-house rat—
is all you were born for to be called that?

(Photo courtesy of Idaho Commission on the Arts)

JERUSALEM
T H E   S P I R I T U A L   Q U E S T

I hope there'll be pine trees in Heaven
And mountains all covered with Snow
With plenty of room to stretch out in,
Like we have here in Idaho.
Written by David H. Smith
and Lorraine S. Wilkinson

The songs in this section celebrate spirituality or morality. *My grandfather was a man of the cloth. His faith was based in the Episcopal Church but drew its strength from the raw, new land of the West.*

The melody of "Jerusalem" calls me back to that faith, back to the ritual and mystery of church celebration: the measured tread, the hooded cross on Good Friday, and the magic blooming of the lilies on Easter and the telling of the Christmas story at midnight in St. Michael's Church—filled with pine and fir boughs. Everyone sings together and finally we go out into the dark-snapping cold with a lighted candle, keeping the flame alive all the way home.

As for the lyrics of this song, William Blake's words struck into my childish imagination with such power
that to this day they still describe for me the fire that persuades human beings to go into uncharted country and build civilizations.

Next to birth and death, the spiritual quest, whether undertaken or internalized, is one of humanity's most undeniable impulses. I always associate this song with my grandfather and his remarkable faith.

—R.S.

141

JERUSALEM

As Sung by Rosalie Sorrels

Written by William Blake

And did those feet in an-cient times walk u-pon Eng-land's plea-sant green?

And was the Ho-ly Lamb of God on Eng-land's plea-sant pas-tures seen?

And did the coun-te-nance di-vine shine forth on Eng-land's cloud-ed hills?

And was Je-ru-sa-lem build-ed there? A-mong those dark Sa-tan-ic

mills?

And did those feet in ancient times
Walk upon England's pleasant green?
And was the Holy Lamb of God
On England's pleasant pasture seen?
And did the countenance divine
Shine forth on England's clouded hills?
And was Jerusalem builded there
Among those dark, Satanic mills?

Bring me my bow of burning gold.
Bring me my arrows of desire.
Bring me my spear . . . Oh, clouds unfold!
Bring me my chariot of fire!
I shall not cease from mental strife . . .
Nor shall my sword rest in my hand . . .
'til we have built Jerusalem
On England's green and pleasant land.

❖❖❖

❖ *I brought "Singing in The Country" to Idaho after living in Utah for thirteen years. I learned the song from Olive Wooley Burt, who told me her mother brought it across the plains during the Mormon trek West. It is a personal example of how deeply songs can affect human lives and how important they can be during our most difficult life experiences. I live in a handmade house my father built on some land his mother and father lived on before I was even born. There was never any money to speak of in our family, but we were always pretty self-sufficient. When Dad went to build this cabin, he simply made everything himself . . . he cut the logs and cured them . . . he made the bricks in the foundation . . . he poured the floor and raised the house—stick by stick and stone by stone.*

The home was pretty bare at first, but he surrounded it with beautiful stonework. My brother, Jim, helped a lot and my mother brought smooth river stones for the patio and planted thyme and mint, wild roses and lilacs. Dad put in aspen trees, junipers, Persian peas, black walnuts . . . I couldn't even begin to name all the growing things around this bowery nest. In any case, you can hardly see it from the road now.

There's a big window by the bed where I sleep, and we had to carry it in by hand, the road being so rough it would have broken otherwise. From that window you can see the road disappear at the bend of Grimes Creek where two tall pine trees stand like sentinels, guarding our domain. My father used to go there every morning to those trees and sing the sun up, like Orpheus. When he died, we put some of his ashes on the basalt stones where the sun's first rays strike into the canyon . . . we put some in the stream and some around the twin pines so that he could forever be the first to greet the dawn. And I sang this song he loved so much for my father . . . I always sing it for him. —R.S.

SINGING IN THE COUNTRY

As Sung by Rosalie Sorrels *Traditional*

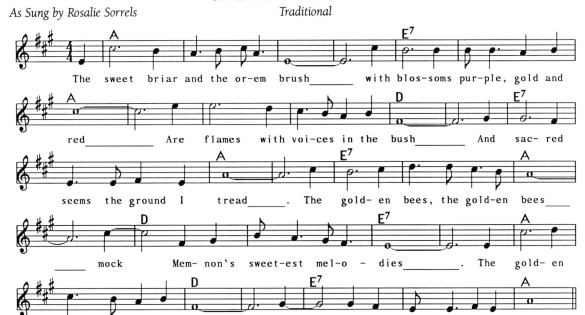

The sweet briar and the or-em brush____ with blos-soms pur-ple, gold and red____ Are flames with voi-ces in the bush____ And sac-red seems the ground I tread____ . The gold-en bees, the gold-en bees____ mock Mem-non's sweet-est mel-o – dies____ . The gold-en bees, the gold-en bees____ mock____ Mem-non's sweet-est mel-o – dies.

The sweet briar and the orem brush,
With blossoms purple, gold, and red,
Are flames with voices in the bush,
And sacred seems the ground I tread.
The golden bees, the golden bees,
Mock Memnon's sweetest melodies.
The golden bees, the golden bees,
Mock Memnon's sweetest melodies.

In shadow of the wood I lie,
Unwaked by dream of noisy mart . . .
Where smoke and dust soil not the sky,
Nor hammers beat on human heart.
Nor shuttles fleet, nor shuttles fleet
Weave life into a winding sheet . . .
Nor shuttles fleet, nor shuttles fleet
Weave life into a winding sheet.

When the pale axeman strikes his stroke
And takes the warm life from my breast,
Plant by my grave a sapling oak
And violets of azure crest.
The oaken staff, the oaken staff,
My shaft; the flowers, my epitaph . . .
The oaken staff, the oaken staff,
My shaft; the flowers, my epitaph.

❖ *Mr. and Mrs. Don Elwell of Preston sent us this song. It is a published piece that expresses in musical* *form a connection between the physical and spiritual landscape of our state.* —R.S.

I HOPE THERE'LL BE PINE TREES IN HEAVEN

Written by David H. Smith and Lorraine S. Wilkinson

I hope there'll be pine trees in Heaven.
And mountains all covered with snow
With plenty of room to stretch out in,
Like we have here in Idaho.

I hope there'll be pine trees in Heaven
To shade the clear streams where they flow
With water that's nectar for drinkin',
Like we have here in Idaho.

I love all the hills, streams, and valleys.
The thought of them gives me a thrill.
And I think I could stand leaving this world
If I knew they could be with me still.

And if there aren't pine trees in Heaven,
I hope there's some place I can go
Where they'll have the things I'll be missin,
'Cause it's Heaven in Idaho.

❖ *Blanche Cowger of Kooskia gave us this song, the words of which she learned from her brother, George* *Presnall, of Troy. Blanche wrote the tune to go with those words.* —R.S.

GOD DOES NOT COMPEL US TO GO

As Sung by Blanche Cowger

When the Can-naan-ites hard-ened their hearts a-gainst God and grieved Him be-cause of their sins, He sent a-long hor-nets to bring them to time and to help his own peo-ple come in. The hor-nets per-suad-ed them that it was best to go quick-ly and not to go slow; They did not com-pel them to go 'gainst their will they just made them wil-ling to go. God does not com-pel us to go. He ne-ver com-pels us to go. God does not com-pel us to go 'gainst our will; He just makes us wil-ling to go.

When the Canaanites hardened their hearts
   against God
And grieved Him because of their sins,
He sent along hornets to bring them to time
And to help his own people come in.

The hornets persuaded them that it was best
To go quickly and not to go slow;
They did not compel them to go 'gainst their will;
They just made them willing to go.

CHORUS:
God does not compel us to go;
He never compels us to go;
God does not compel us to go 'gainst our will;
He just makes us willing to go.

If a nest of live hornets were bro't to this room,
And the creatures allowed to go free,
You would not need urging to make yourself scarce;
You'd want to get out, don't you see?

They would not lay hold and by force of their
   strength,
Throw you out of the window, oh, no!
They would not compel you to go 'gainst your will,
They'd just make you willing to go.

When Jonah was sent to the work of the Lord
The outlook was not very bright.
He never had done such a hard thing before,
So he backed and ran off from the fight.

Now God sent a big fish to swallow him up;
The storm I'm sure you all know
He did not compel him to go 'gainst his will
He just made him willing to go.

❖ *In Idaho Folklife, Homesteads to Headstones (1985), Louie Attebery quotes folklorist Polly Stewart as saying: "Playing cards have been important in the image stock of folk poets for centuries and the figure shows up everywhere from Middle-English poems to country-western songs." Here the four suits represent what the poet saw as important parts of human experience—fortune, love, war, death.*

Bryan Bundy sang this song at our Lewiston song swap. The Bundy Family is an Idaho singing family with a repertoire of traditional songs. —R.S.

A GAME OF CARDS

As Sung by Bryan Bundy　　　　　　　*Traditional*

This life is but a game of cards which each one has to learn. Each shuf-fles, cuts, and deals the pack, and each a trump doth turn.

This life is but a game of cards which each one has to learn;
Each shuffles, cuts, and deals the pack, and each a trump
　　doth turn.

When diamonds chance to crown the pack, 'tis then men stake
　　their gold;
Large sums have oft been won and lost by gamblers young and old.

When hearts are trump we play for love, and pleasure rules the
　　hour;
Two hearts have ofttimes been made one while in a rosy bower.

When clubs are trump, look out for war, on ocean and on land,
For many a bloody deed's been done while the club was in the
　　hand.

And then at last is he turned up by the busy hand of time;
'Tis he who endeth every age in every land and clime.

For no matter how much a man may win, nor how much a man may
　　save,
We find the spade turns up at last to dig each gambler's grave.

146

❖ Like the song "God Does Not Compel Us To Go," we found "Payday" and "A Drunkard's Ode" in Blanche Cowger's great collection. Both of these songs reflect a strong strain of western morality. They feature choice: retribution for a life misspent on earth or eternal glory for a life of Christian virtue. —R.S.

A DRUNKARD'S ODE

How well do I remember,
'Twas in the late November,
I was walking down the street
Quite full of pride;
My heart was all a-flutter,
As I slipped down in the gutter,
And a pig came there
And laid down by my side;
As I lay there in the gutter,
All too soused to even mutter,
A lady passing by
Was heard to say:
"One may tell a brute that boozes

By the company he chooses."
Hearing this, the pig got up
And slowly walked away.

❖❖❖

❖ I learned this one from my maternal grandfather, James Madison Kelly (Twin Falls), who died when I was nine years old—but I remember him better than anyone I've ever met. My mother thinks he learned this song when he was a roustabout for minstrel shows in the mid-west. —R.S.

RUN, MARY, RUN

As Sung by Rosalie Sorrels

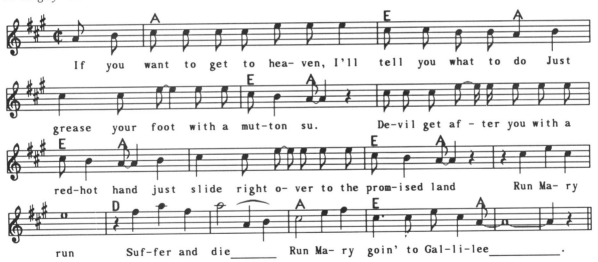

If you want to get to hea-ven, I'll tell you what to do Just grease your foot with a mut-ton su. De-vil get af-ter you with a red-hot hand just slide right o-ver to the prom-ised land Run Ma-ry run Suf-fer and die Run Ma-ry goin' to Gal-li-lee

If you want to get to heaven, I'll tell you what to do
Grease your foot with a mutton su
Devil get after you with a red hot hand
Just slide right over to the promised land

CHORUS:
Run, Mary, run
Suffer and die
Run, Mary, run
Goin' to Galilee.

Some come a limpin' and some come lame . . .
Some come a runnin' in religion's name . . .
Mind now sister how you walk across . . .
Your foot might slip and your soul get lost . . .
so . . .

CHORUS:

❖ *Blanche Cowger (Kooskia) told us that she learned* *this song from her mother, Hazel E. Presnall, who* "*often sang it as a special at church."* —R.S.

PAYDAY

As Sung by Blanche Cowger

You may talk about your jolly good times
And the life you love to live
As you go in for every thing
The world and the Devil can give.
You may work or rest as suits you best
And so live out your day;
But I'll give you a pointer about my choice:
I'm in for a life that pays.

CHORUS:
On that final payday to which we all must come
The Lord will pay the wages for the work which you have done,
But the wages of sin is death, you know;
Not any of that for me,
For there's nothing but evil in serving the devil
On Payday, don't you see?

It is not every Saturday night the Lord squares his account.
It is not at the end of the month you receive your full amount,
But the soul that has lived in sin and shame has not drawn
    all its pay,
But alas you will find with interest compound laid up
    against that day.

CHORUS:
So think before you sell your soul for the sin you love so well.
Will it pay my friend for you to spend eternity in Hell?
You never can live life over again when it is wasted away,
So hasten to choose or your soul you will lose and I ask you will
    it pay?

CHORUS:

*(Photo courtesy of Idaho
Commission on the Arts)*

149

❖ *Carmen Totorica learned this in Guernica in the 1930's. She says it was very popular and people sang it in the streets. It was written by a black Portuguese painter who married a white woman with whom he had one child.* —R.S.

LOS ANGELITOS NEGROS

As Sung by Carmen Totorica

Written by Antonio Machin

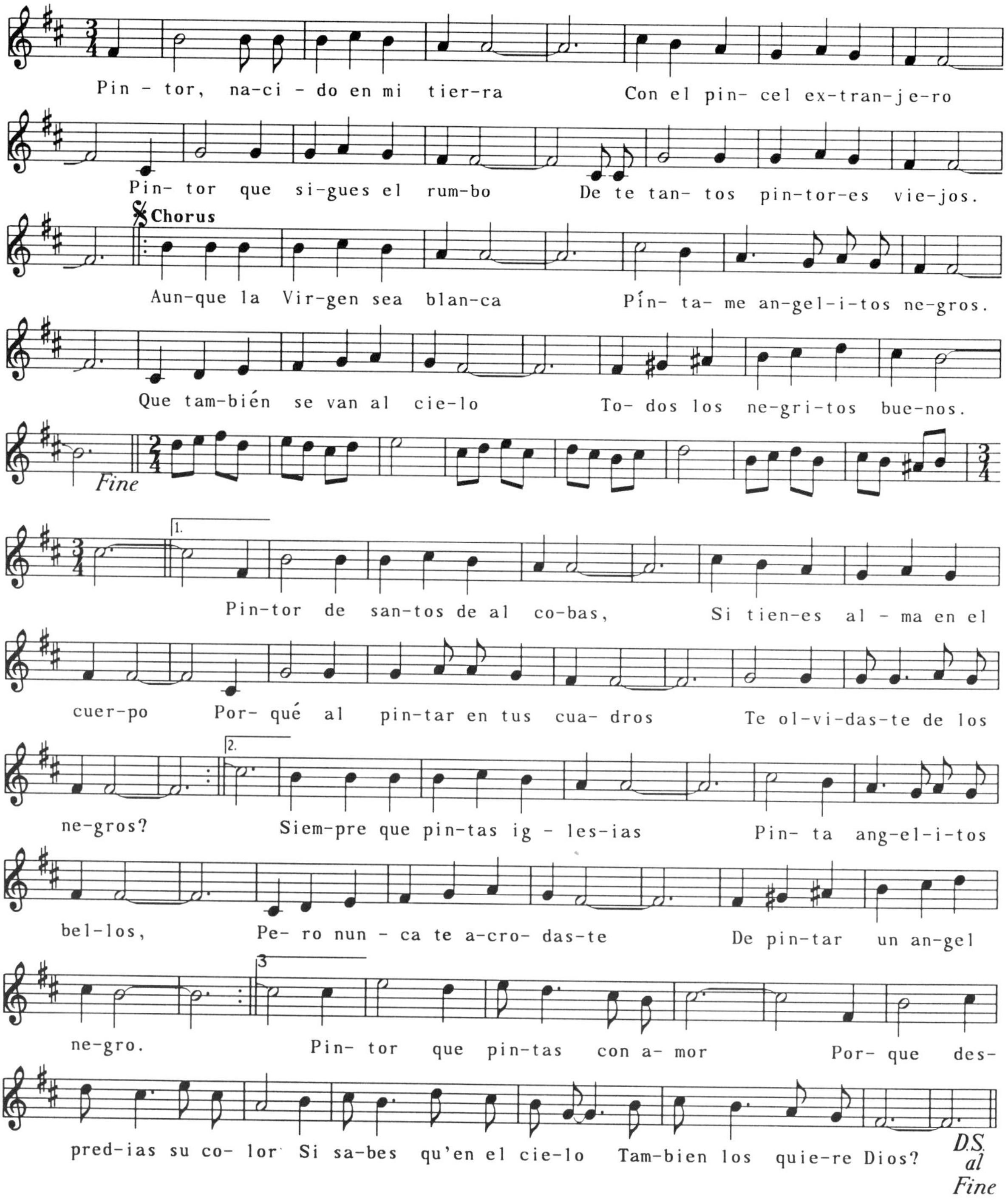

Pin - tor, na-ci - do en mi tier-ra Con el pin- cel ex-tran-j e-ro
Pin- tor que si-gues el rum-bo De te tan- tos pin-tor-es vie-jos.
Chorus
Aun-que la Vir-gen sea blan-ca Pín- ta- me an-gel-i-tos ne-gros.
Que tam-bién se van al cie-lo To- dos los ne-gri-tos bue-nos.
Fine
1.
Pin-tor de san-tos de al co-bas, Si tien-es al - ma en el
cuer-po Por- qué al pin-tar en tus cua- dros Te ol-vi-das-te de los
ne-gros?
2.
Siem-pre que pin-tas ig - les-ias Pin- ta ang-el-i-tos
bel-los, Pe- ro nun - ca te a-cro- das-te De pin-tar un an-gel
ne-gro.
3
Pin- tor que pin-tas con a- mor Por- que des-
pred-ias su co- lor Si sa-bes qu'en el cie-lo Tam-bien los quie-re Dios?
D.S. al Fine

Pintor nacido en mi tierra
Con el pincel extranjero
Pintor que sigues el rumbo
De te tantos pintores viejos.

CHORUS:
Aunque la Virgen sea blanca
Píntame angelitos negros.
Que también se van al cielo
Todos los negritos buenos.

Pintor de santos de alcobas,
Si tienes alma en el cuerpo
Porqué al pintar en tus cuadros
Te olvidaste de los negros?

Siempre que pintas iglesias
Pinta angelitos bellos,
Pero nunca te acordaste
De pintar un angel negro.

Pintor que pintas con amor
Porque despredias su color
Si sabes que en el cielo
Tambien los quiere Dios?

Painter born in my country
With a palette from a foreign country
Painter who follows the ways
Of many old-time painters.

CHORUS:
Although the Virgin is white
Paint for me some black angels
Because good blacks
Also go to heaven.

Painter of saints for displays
If you have a heart in your body
Why did you forget the blacks
When you were painting your paintings?

When you paint for churches
You paint beautiful angels
But never did you remember
To paint a black angel.

Painter, you paint with love
Why do you deprecate the color black
If you know that in heaven
We are also loved by God?

Greek Orthodox Church, Boise. (Photo courtesy of Idaho State Historical Society)

❖ *In Stories of Our Mormon Hymms (1975), J. Spencer Cornall quotes Charles W. Penrose, the author of "O Ye Mountains High" as stating, "'O Ye Mountains High' was written somewhere along about 1854, published in 1856: 'I was walking on a dusty road in Essex. My toes were blistered and my heels, too. I had been promised that if I would stay in the mission field another year I should be released. That was the cry every year: "Brother Penrose, if you will stay and labor another year, we will see that you are released to go to Zion." But it kept up for over ten years. Of course I had read about Zion and heard about the streets of Salt Lake City, with the clear streams of water on each side of the street, with shade trees, and so on. I could see it in my mind's eye and set it to a tune—the Scotch ditty, 'O Minnie, O Minnie, Come o'er The Lea'; those were the opening words. When I got to the place called Mundon, in Essex, we held a cottage meeting, and in that meeting I sang it for the first time it was ever sung. Of course the words were adapted to a person who had never been to Zion then, but it was afterwards changed in a very slight respect or two, to fit people who had gathered with the Saints. It was inspirational and seemed to please President Brigham Young.'"* —R.S.

O YE MOUNTAINS HIGH

Written by Charles W. Penrose

Oh ye moun - tains high where the clear blue sky Ar- ches o - ver the vales of the free, Where the pure breez-es blow and the clear stream- lets flow, How I've longed to your bos - om to flee!

O Zion! dear Zion! Land of the free, Now my own mountain home, unto thee I have come; All my fond hopes are centered in thee.

O ye mountains high, where the clear blue sky
Arches over the vales of the free,
Where the pure breezes blow and the clear streamlets flow,
How I've longed to your bosom to flee!
O Zion! dear Zion! Land of the free,
Now my own mountain home, unto thee I have come;
All my fond hopes are centered in thee.

Tho the great and the wise all thy beauties despise,
To the humble and pure thou art dear;
Tho the haughty may smile and the wicked revile,
Yet we love thy glad tidings to hear.
O Zion! dear Zion! home of the free,
Tho thou wert forced to fly to thy chambers on high,
Yet we'll share joy and sorrow with thee.

In thy mountain retreat, God will strengthen thy feet;
Without fear of thy foes thou shalt tread;
And their silver and gold, as the prophets have told,
Shall be brought to adorn thy fair head.
O Zion! dear Zion! home of the free,
Soon thy towers shall shine with a splendor divine,
And eternal thy glory shall be.

Here our voices we'll raise, and we'll sing to thy praise,
Sacred home of the prophets of God.
Thy deliverance is nigh, thy oppressors shall die;
And thy land shall be freedom's abode.
O Zion! dear Zion land of the free,
In thy temples we'll bend;
All thy rights we'll defend;
And our home shall be ever with thee.

❖ *My grandmother Arabelle Beaire Kelly was a Methodist and I've always loved this camp meeting song. This version came from Blanche Cowger's friend Dollie Lewis, who sang with us in Blanche's trailer in Kooskia.* —R.S.

METHODIST PIE

As Sung by Dollie Lewis

Well, we went down a camp meet-in' the other afternoon
for to hear them shout and sing.
For to tell each other how they love one another
and to make hal-le-lu-jah-ring.
There's old Uncle Daniel and his mother;
Ebenezer; Uncle Rufus and his lame gal, Sue;
There's Polly and Melindy, and there's old mother Bendro

you never seen a happier crew.
Well they all go there for to have a good time
but eat that grub so sly.
Have applesauce butter with the sugar in the gourd
and a great big Methodist pie.

Oh, little children I believe.
Oh, little children I believe
Oh, little children I believe I'm a Methodist til I die.

Bird Goodwin is a local singer in Orofino who epitomizes the hospitality and friendliness of her north Idaho community. Her deep affection for the region and its people is reflected in the "Old Fashioned Sunday" celebration which she organizes each year.
(Photo courtesy of Michael Cordell)

❖ *Bird Goodwin sang this song for us at the Orofino Song Swap. She says, "This song is so special because it expressed for many of us what we believe to be the real place to find God—out among the nature He created. This is timber country and the words fit what we see and feel every day. This song is a favorite at Sunrise Services and any gathering held outdoors."* —R.S.

THE PLACE WHERE I WORSHIP

As Sung by Bird Goodwin

Oh the place where I worship is the wide open spaces,
Built by the hand of the Lord!
Where the trees of the forest are like pipes of an organ
And the breeze plays an A-men chord.
Oh the stars are the candles and they light up the mountains,
Mountains are altars of God.
Oh the place where I worship is the wide open spaces,
Where the sun warms the peaceful sod.
There's a carpet of green and a sky-blue roof above;
I'm welcome there alone, or with the one I love.
In your heart take a good look,
If you follow the Good Book,
You're sure to find your reward.
Oh the place where I worship is the wide open spaces,
Built by the hand of the Lord.

One hill of potatoes grown by J. R. Newton.(Photo courtesy of Idaho State Historical Society)

IDAHOEDOWN

LOCAL MUSIC, LOCAL DANCE

Oh vast earth apple, waiting to be fried,
Of all the starers the most many-eyed,
What furtive purpose hatched you long ago
In Indiana or in Idaho?
Peter Viereck

This is the provincial section of our Idaho collection . . .

Our license plates have said, "Idaho Famous Potatoes"; there is a working band called "Famous Potatoes"; and there is a book of Idaho writers called "Famous Potatoes"; and there is a wonderful poem by Peter Vierick called, "The Sinister Potato."

Polynesians have pineapples, people in New Guinea have yams, here in Idaho we have spuds. Maybe that's why so many people confuse Idaho with Iowa—they have corn. What I like about having a potato for a symbol is its simplicity. We don't have patriotic volunteers (Tennessee) or dramatic bucking broncos

(Wyoming), we've got something that comes right out of the ground and tastes good with butter and gravy on it. In spite of its blatant commercialism, I like it. When they trade the potato for a fir tree or a fly fisherman, look out, 'cause Idaho won't be what it used to be.

—R.S.

SALMON STUFFED IDAHOS
(from *Stanley Basin and Sawtooth Valley Cookbook*, 1976)

6 medium-size Idaho potatoes
1/3 cup hot milk
1 egg, well beaten
1 teaspoon salt
1/4 teaspoon paprika
1/8 teaspoon cayenne
1 tablespoon lemon juice
1 1/2 cups cooked salmon . . . flaked
1/3 cup minced onions
2 tablespoons butter or oleo

Bake the potatoes. Remove from oven and split in halves lengthwise. Scoop out the inside part, taking care not to break the shells. Mash the scooped out portion. Add the milk, well-beaten egg, salt, paprika, cayenne, lemon juice, salmon, and onions which have been sauteed in butter. Mix well. Refill the potato shells with buttered crumbs, and bake in a moderate over (350 degrees) for about 20 minutes.

—Jody Milligan

TO A SINISTER POTATO
By Peter Viereck

Oh vast earth apple, waiting to be fried,
Of all life's starers the most many-eyed,
What furtive purpose hatched you long ago
In Indiana or in Idaho?

In Indiana and in Idaho
Snug underground the great potatoes grow,
Puffed up with secret paranoias unguessed
By all the duped and starch-fed middle west.

Like coiled up springs or like a will-to-power,
The fat and earthy lurkers bide their hour,
The silent watchers of our raucous show
In Indiana and in Idaho.

"They think us dull, a food and not a flower,
Wait! We'll outshine all roses in our hour.
Not wholesomeness but mania swells us so
In Indiana and Idaho."

"In each Kiwanis club on every plate
So bland and health exuding do we wait
That Indiana never, never knows
How much we envy stars and hate the rose."

Some doom will strike (as all potatoes know)
When, once too often mashed in Idaho,
From its cocoon the drabbest of earth's powers
Rises and is a star
   And shines
   And lours.

(l to r) Senator William E. Borah, Honorable Fred T. Dubois, Dr. W. N. Johannessen, Idaho State Society, 1926.(Photo courtesy of Idaho State Historical Society)

Lincoln County Fair, 1989. (Photo courtesy of Idaho Commission on the Arts)

(Photo courtesy of Idaho State Historical Society)

161

❖ *Chane and Kathy Mattoon from Grangeville wrote the words and music to "Idahoe-down": "A lot of people know the song here in central Idaho from listening to our band," Kathy says, "They occasionally play it on the local radio stations. Chane had the idea for 'Idahoe-down.' I thought about it for a while and wrote it about my grandpa. I'd always listened to him play the fiddle when I was growing up. He really knew* how to make that fiddle sing. His name was Robert Pickett.

"We have a country band named 'The Chane Gang Band.' We sing around central Idaho for rodeos, town celebrations, fairs, etc. It's fun to watch the people get out and dance while you're playing. Chane got the idea for the song watching the people 'hoe-it-down.' We figured there are songs about Texas, Tennessee, etc. Why not write a song about Idaho?" —R.S.

IDAHOE-DOWN

Words and Music by Chane and Kathy Mattoon

Well ya heard-a that Tex-as Two-step, And ole Cot-ton-eyed Joe. Let me tell ya 'bout a-noth-er dance done by the folks in I-da-ho. Well this here dance step, it's real sim-ple you can see. You just clap your hands and stomp your feet, and wig-gle at the knees. And do the I-da-hoe-down, Take a look and you'll see. The I-da hoe-down, One foot, two foot, three. I-da-hoe-down, It's as ea-sy as can be, Just clap your hands and stomp your feet, and wig-gle at the knees.

Well ya heard a that Texas two step and ole cotton-eyed Joe,
Let me tell ya 'bout another dance done by the folks in Idaho.
Well this here dance step . . . its real simple you can see:
You just clap your hands and stomp your feet and wiggle
   at the knee.

CHORUS:
And do the Idahoe-down, take a look and you'll see.
Idahoe-down one foot, two foot, three;
Idahoe-down it's as easy as can be,
Just clap your hands, stomp your feet and wiggle at the knees.

I remember watchin' grandpa when I was just a kid,
He'd take down that old tattered case and open up the lid;
Resin up his fiddle bow and all the folks come gather 'round.
He'd warm up on the Devils Dream and play the Idahoe-down.

CHORUS:
Do the Idahoe-down, take a look and you'll see.
Idahoe-down one foot, two foot, three;
Idahoe-down it's as easy as can be,
Just clap your hands, and stomp your feet and wiggle at the knees.

So now we play it at all the country spots;
The good ones don't ya know.
But the best place that we played it at is here at home in Idaho.
And that's where we see it and all the folks come gather 'round;
They clap their hands and stomp their feet and do the Idahoe-down.

CHORUS:
Do the Idahoe-down, take a look and you'll see.
Idahoe-down one foot, two foot, three;
Idahoe-down it's as easy as can be,
Ya just clap your hands, stomp your feet and wiggle at the knees.

Its the Idahoe-down take a look and you'll see.
The Idahoe-down one foot, two foot, three;
Idahoe-down come on and hoe it down with me,
You just clap your hands and stomp your feet do the one foot, two
   foot, three.

I was a friend to Fred Keefer for a score of years. He welcomed me into his home and showed me his mementos and explained them to me. This poem was a distillation of all those visits to his home and the feeling *it gave me every time I went there. Fred was really one of those who spanned the years from the old to the new and his kind will not be again.*

—Quincy M. Jensen
(Idaho Falls)

AT FRED'S
By Quincy M. Jensen

I walk through this place in the twilight
   And the memories crowd one on one.
The skull of a Chinese miner,
   A holstered outlaw gun.

Great books that hold the story
   Of a land both new and free,
And a promise bold, to young and old,
   A NEW life in this wild country.
A high chair for Frank and one for Fred
   Stand in the corner there,
With marks of teeth and pounding spoons
   And a mother's tender care.

The ten-gallon Stetsons all in a row
   With sweat bands stained and brown,
Were a shield for sun and wind and rain
   Before they were put down.

A pack saddle hangs on a peg by the door,
   Its girth straps shiny and bright
For a horse that's crossed the Great Divide,
   It waits through the long, long night.

And now on toward the twilight,
   When sight and sound grow dim,
May his horse be gentle, the valley lush
   In that cowboy heaven for him.

❖ *I have pulled together in this part of the book a number of songs from the massive collection of folk songs compiled by Stella Hendren. The Hendren Collection (which was used by Austin Fife in all of his books) is just that—like salt shakers—a collection. There is no information, no one sang them for us, it is just albums and folders filled with songs taken from letters, magazines, and newspapers. Many of the people we met during our tours had collections like this. I have also added to these lyrics and poems some words and recipes that reflect terms and foods unique to the Idaho experience.* —R.S.

ON THE TRAIL TO IDAHO
(From Stella Hendren, Kooskia, Idaho)

I met the boss; he wanted me to go
Help drive his herd to Idaho.
I told the boss it was out of my range,
But if he had the price, I was about to change.

We started out the first of May;
Everything looked good, everything was gay.
We rolled along just like a ball
Until one night we had a squall.

The cattle stampeded all over the ground;
We couldn't get them all to lay down.
We drove for days and sometimes weeks,
We couldn't see nothing but the mountain peaks.

The sand did roll and fill my eyes,
And I thought of home and almost cried.
We crossed three rivers we didn't know,
Out on the trail to Idaho.

It was a long and lonesome go
Out on the trail to Idaho.
We saw some Indians; they were on the run;
They were kinder jubus of our needle guns.

They divided up in twos and fours,
They didn't like old forty-fours.
When I got home I told the boys
Out on that run they'd see no joys.

Long stretches we drove was very dry,
All the water we drank was alkali.
I made up my mind when back on the range
Not to scamper off after the little extra change.
  Go 'long, Blue Dog.

THE BOYS AND GIRLS OF IDAHO
From the Stella Hendren collection
(Sung to the Tune of "Oh, Tannenbaum")

The boys and girls of Idaho, Idaho, oh Idaho,
They'll make the sheep and chickens grow,
  In Idaho, oh Idaho.
They'll can the fruit and dry the corn;
They'll help their Daddies on the farm;
They'll work at eve; they'll work at morn,
  In Idaho, oh Idaho.

The boys and girls in Idaho, Idaho, oh Idaho,
They'll keep the weeds from every row,
  In Idaho, oh Idaho.
They'll grow the pigs that can't be beat,
And Idaho shan't want for meat;
They'll put the farmers on their feet,
  In Idaho, oh Idaho.

The boys and girls in Idaho, Idaho, oh Idaho,
The girls are learning how to sew,
  In Idaho, oh Idaho.
Of spuds the clubs will raise a crop,
So Idaho will be on top,

They'll grow the beets so they can't stop,
  In Idaho, oh Idaho.

FOR HER I'D LEAVE VIRGINIA
(From the Hendren Collection)

For her I'd leave Virginia
I'd leave my Mary Land,
I'd part with Mrs. Sippi,
The widow fair and bland.

I'd leave my Louisa Anna
And other Anna, too;
I'd bid farewell to George
Though Georgia would be true.

I'd part with Minna Sota,
I'd part with Della Ware.
I'd leave brunette Miss Souri
Or the Carolina pair.

These women are all lovely,
True-hearted girls, I know,
But I'd give them all the go-by
And cleave the Ida Ho.

I like her breezy manners,
I like her honest ways,
I like her in the moonlight,
I like her sunny days.

Good-bye, my own Virginia
And other girls I know,
I'm hanging round the gatepost
Of a girl named Idaho Ho!

UP IN IDAHO
By John Huckins

1st CHORUS:
There's a Big Wood River, there's a Silver Creek
There's a Copper Basin wide and deep.
There's a Baldy Mountain, there's a Warm Springs line
And a wide blue sky where the sun shines most o' the time

VERSE:
Rolled into Ketchum one autumn afternoon
Didn't have the money to pay for a motel room
Walked a half-mile north o' town
Threw my sleepin' bag right on the ground
Woke up next mornin' on top of Ernie Hemingway's grave

2nd CHORUS:
There's a Stanley Basin, there's a Smiley Creek
There's the Sawtooth Mountains sharp and steep
There's the Salmon River, there's the lodgepole pine
And a wide blue sky where the sun shines most o' the time

VERSE:
Folks all say he loved the autumn time of year
He hunted and he fished with friends that he held dear
He was a ramblin' man through the world
But a country boy first of all
Ketchum was his favorite place when the leaves would fall

1st CHORUS:
VERSE.

I got the promise of a job way down on 'Frisco Bay
Should be pullin' out o' Ketchum—any day
But California's gonna have to wait
Like a trout I've taken the bait
An' I gotta find out what Idaho's all about

2nd CHORUS TO FINISH

CURLY JOE FROM IDAHO
(From the Hendren Collection)

Let me tell you a tale of a gamblin' man,
The roughest and toughest of all—
He was Curly Joe from Idaho,
He was rough and rugged and tall.
He was over six feet and as slim as a rail
And his eyes were as black as the night,
And when he cut loose that on'ry cayuse
Would always end up in a fight.

CHORUS:
Oh Curly Joe from Idaho,
A ramblin' gamblin' rover—
He dealt from the bottom,
   He dealt from the top
   But now his dealin' is over.

One night he stormed into the Bootheel Saloon
And roared with a voice big and loud,
"Come on everyone we're in for some fun
I'm buying the drinks for the crowd."
The gamblin' stopped while they all took a drink
To the health of old Curly Joe—
He drank to content and over he went
To the table that had the most dough.

He rested his arm on the table of green
And asked for a parcel of draw,
They dealt him a deuce, a trey and a queen,
The worst hand that he'd ever saw.

Then came two more cards, a four and a five
That left him needin' a six;
But they dealt him an eight
That ruined his straight,
Now he knew they were up to their tricks.

Then he asked for the deal
And he picked up the cards
And rip—they fell in their places,
And then from the middle, the bottom and top
He dealt off those four fatal aces.
He knew at a glance he was bettin' his pants
So his dough he laid on the line
And he said, "If you please,
I'll just play these
I think this hand's mighty fine":

They made all their bets
And they spread their cards
Upon the table of green.
Then old Curly Joe raked over the dough,
Four aces were over four queens.

Then a shot rang out in the Bootheel Saloon
And poor Curly fell to the floor.
He whispered and sighed,
"Somebody has lied
Four aces don't win anymore."

❖❖❖

❖ *John Carrey, of Riggins, tells an accompanying story about being hired to make a song for the Townsend Plan, an economic development plan which would have given each citizen $200 that had to be spent and, thus, theoretically would stimulate the economy. There was a contest to find a song for promotion of the Townsend Plan. He only got to sing the one verse before they threw him out.*

   "I composed this (if that is what you call it)," John told us,"in the 1930's in a sheep camp up Big Salmon."

—R.S.

TOWNSEND PLAN SONG
Well I'll get that two hundred, then I know what I'll do . . .
I'll get me a sweetheart with two hundred too.
With four hundred cart wheels we'll roll down the line
With a good lookin' chauffeur I'm a-buyin' the wine.

Bud Baltazor was my grandfather. I collected his stories and photographs into a book entitled Last of the Mustangs and Jerkline Skinners *(Schwartz Printing: Nampa, Idaho; 1976). The songs in the book were made up to tell stories of familiar surroundings and events. I do not doubt that grandpa made these lyrics up. The form and tune were probably popular or familiar ones of that time. I do not have the tune to "Dig Me a Grave in the Owyhees."* —Jerry Baltazor
Shoshone

DIG ME A GRAVE IN THE OWYHEES
By Bud Baltazor

Dig me a grave in the Owyhees
Out where a tired man can rest.
Bury my saddle beside me
With a corn-licker' jug on my chest.
Hide me away in the Owyhees
Don't put no stone at my head.
Hide me where my wife can't find me
And I'll live in peace when I'm dead.
I'll take my saddle mustangin'
Drink from my jug when I'm dry.
Well now it's dig me a grave in the Owyhees
But don't throw me in till I die.

Oh bury me out in the Owyhees
Where the hooves of the horses will fall over me
Where their echoing tread passes over my head
I'm a mustanger from the Owyhees
Where the wild mustangs prowl, the coyotes
     they howl
Where the birds will make music for me
Where the long shadows fall and the turtle
     doves call
There I'll rest forever in peace.

❖ *Chuck Eixenberger (Post Falls) started hunting elk at age twelve outside Kellogg. He says, "The Idaho Fish and Game Department, with cooperation from the U.S. Forest Service, has managed to provide an abundant yearly harvest of elk."* —R.S.

EIXENBERGER'S IDAHOAN ELK BALLS WITH WILD MUSHROOMS

Ingredients:
1 rifle
1 elk grunt tube
1 pair vibram sole logging boots
1 flashlight
1 pint Jack Daniels whiskey
1 4x4 truck
1 green pepper
1 cup wild mushrooms
1 can Eixenberger's special herbs and spices
1 cup sour cream

Directions:

Step 1. On a Friday afternoon in September, load the items listed above 4x4 truck into the truck. Drive to within 1 hour's walking distance of at least 5 elk. You will know when you're there because of the telltale signs such as:

1. So many 4x4 trucks along the road you have trouble parking yours.

2. At least two horses tied up alongside the road.

3. Fat men splitting wood and building large camp fires.

(Note: Items 2 and 3 can be replaced with loud rock 'n roll music and skinny men drinking beer and playing poker.)

Ignore the people, try to figure out where you are on a map, then go straight to bed.

Step 2. Wakeup Saturday morning at 4 a.m. The fat men and/or the poker players should be asleep by now. Do not cook bacon, do not cook eggs, just grab the items from Step 1 (except the whiskey) and using the flashlight, walk *away* from the road you drove in on until daylight.

Step 3. Grunt on elk tube and listen for a response.

Step 4. Wander around (you should be hungry by now) and pretend you're an elk and start looking for some nice fresh brush to munch on. Listen for an elk to bugle. If one bugles, run towards him (usually uphill) at approximately 20 MPH (any slower and he'll get wind of you).

Step 5. Repeat steps 4 and 5 until 9:30 a.m. or you have bagged an elk. Then go back to your truck and cook breakfast. It should be nice and peaceful at camp now.

Step 6. Drink 3 oz. of whiskey, then start looking for wild mushrooms. This can be done right from your truck, looking out the window as you drive through groves of cedars near stream beds.

Step 7. Repeat steps 2 to 6 until you have 1 cup of wild mushrooms and 500 pounds of elk meat.

Step 8. Go home and can the mushrooms, dropping the elk off at a butcher shop. Have the butcher save 1 pound of elk burger for your gourmet elk balls.

Step 9. Take the elk burger, green peppers and special seasoning and mix thoroughly. Then make meat balls the size of golf balls and brown in a hot fry pan.

Step 10. Take mushrooms and sour cream and prepare the sauce. Add meat balls and let simmer.

Wood family fishing trip, Payette Lakes, turn of the century. (Photo courtesy of Idaho State Historical Society)

Three men with a bear. (Photo courtesy of Bonner County Historical Society)

170

IDAHO SPEECH
(From Vardis Fisher's *Idaho Lore*, 1939)

As big as a skinned ox: usually applied to persons.

As low as a hog's belly: depressed; down at the mouth.

Bob-wire: barbed wire.

Brush-whip: to rebuke mildly.

Busier than Hattie's flea: extremely busy.

Catty-cornered: cater-cornered.

Chin-music: incessant (and usually empty) talk.

Clear-grit: the genuine article.

Cut of your jib: a contemptuous appraisal of character or personality.

Doodlebug: unscrupulous mine promoter.

Doughgod: a chunk of (usually) baking-powder bread.

Fat as a hen's forehead: meager.

Give it a lick and a promise: to do carelessly.

Gunsight lode: an ore lode found and then lost.

Hairow: horror.

Hell beating tanbark: hasten; to go in a hurry.

Hightailing: to go swiftly. The expression comes from the fact that horses raise their tails high fleeing.

Hit the high lonesome: to depart, usually in haste; or to set out for an unknown destination.

In spite of hell and high water: in spite of all obstacles.

In the lurks: in the lurch.

Knight of the road: stagecoach robber.

Made the riffle: was successful.

Make a poor mouth: plead poverty.

Mormon candy: raw carrot.

Mormon rain: a dust storm.

Mouth-almighty: boastful.

Not on your tintype: emphatic refusal.

Ragtag and bobtail: odds and ends.

Rigs: wagons or other vehicles.

Rig out: to prepare, usually for a journey.

Ring-boned, knock-kneed, and spavined: an expression of contempt or uselessness.

Scringe: to cringe.

Slept on a buffalo robe: slept on the earth.

Sourdough: old-timer.

Spell: a short period of time; to spell equals to change off, to take turns with a person laboring; or to spell a beast laboring, meaning to allow it to rest.

Stand up to the rock: face the situation.

Starkled: startled.

Stick a pin there: make a note of it.

Summer foller: summer fallow.

Sweethearten a girl: to woo.

Swivel: shrivel.

They fit: they fought.

Till hell wouldn't have it: the expression may mean thoroughly used up; or beaten or vanquished.

To goak: to goad.

To fork: to mount (usually) a horse; "He forked his horse."

To hef: to estimate weight of by lifting.

To kick the wind: to cut capers.

To light and set: to dismount and talk awhile.

To lallygag: to flirt.

Tough it out: endure.

Vent the brand: change ownership.

Whip the devil around the stump: to indulge in self-excuses.

Whitetop: a buggy.

❖❖❖

IDAHO POTATOES

In the Snake River Valley lives an old-timer who is known as Old Jim. Old Jim comes to town now and then and boasts of the fertility of his land, but complains that he is unable to market the stuff. He grew pumpkins, but they were so large he could not get them on to a wagon, and then ventured into potatoes. When, two years ago, a CCC camp was established near by, Old Jim was approached by a man who wanted to buy a hundred pounds of spuds. "Only a hundred pounds?" he asked, scratching his pate. "No, I can't do it. I wouldn't cut a spud in two for no one."

—Vardis Fisher, *Idaho Lore*

Mrs. W. R. Butler (Ann Wakeman) with daughter Katherine, Atlanta, Idaho.(Photo courtesy of Idaho State Historical Society)

WOMEN OF THE WEST

HEROINES, HURDY-GURDIES AND FASHIONABLE WOMEN

I'll always stand up for the women
Though they say they are the mother of sin.
'Tis only a false accusation —
A willful invention of men.
He was only a four-flushing gambler
Who went broke at his own game
And laid it on to a woman
That she might bear the blame.

Idaho Jack Treadwell

Women have never come off very well in traditional folk songs. I've always hated for example, the jealous lover ballad, the "love 'em and leave 'em" cowboy romance ballads, and the songs about the bad girl with the heart of gold who everybody loves and nobody will marry.

The most popular themes of the women's songs in general collections were either, "I wonder when I shall be married?" or, "I wish I was single again." When you look at the larger picture, however, women emerge as tough, independent, and possessed of a remarkable sense of humor, particularly the women of the West.

A New York journalist once used this 1862 quote from Anthony Trollope to describe my western femininity. I took it as a compliment:

"I cannot imagine myself much in love with a
lady in the (American) west. They are as sharp as nails, but then they are also as hard. They know so much more that they ought to know. They are tyrants to their parents, and never practice the virtue of obedience 'til they have half grown-up daughters of their own. They have faith in the destiny of their country, if in nothing else; but they believe that destiny is to be worked out by the spirit and talent of the young women. I can forgive Eve in that she tempted Adam to eat the apple. Had she come from the West country she would have ordered him to make his meal, and then I could not have forgiven her."

—R.S.

173

Take ninety pounds of flesh and bone, mainly bones, wash clean and bore holes in the ears, bend the neck to conform with the Grecian bend, the Boston dip, the kangaroo droop, the Saratoga slope or the bullfrog beak, as the taste inclines. Then add three yards of linen, one hundred yards of ruffles and seventy-five yards of edging, eighteen yards of dimity, one pair of silk-cotton hose with patent hip attachments, one pair of false calves, six yards of flannel, embroidered, one pair Balmoral boots with heels three inches high, four pounds whale bone in strips, seventeen hundred and sixty yards of steel wire, three-quarters of a mile of tape, ten pounds of raw cotton or two wire hemispheres, one wire basket that would hold a bushel, four copies of the World, one hundred and fifty yards of silk or other dress goods, five hundred yards of lace, fourteen hundred yards fringe and other trimmings, twelve gross of buttons, one box pearl face powder, one saucer of carmine and an old hare's foot, one bushel of false hair frizzed and fretted la maniaque, one bundle Japanese switches with rats, mice and other varmints, one peck of hairpins, one lace handkerchief, nine inches square, with patent holder. Perfume with attar of roses or "Blessed Baby" or "West End." Stuff the head with fashionable novels, ball tickets, playbills, wedding-cards, some scandal, a lot of wasted time and a very little sage. Add a half-grain of common sense, three scruples of religion and a modicum of modesty. Season with vanity, affectation and folly. Garnish with earrings, finger rings, breastpins, chains, bracelets, feathers and flowers to suit the taste. Pearls and diamonds may be added and pinchbeck from the dollar-store will do.

Whirl all around in a fashionable circle and stew by gaslight for six hours.

This dish is highly ornamental, a *piéce de résistance* for the head of your table upon grand occasions but, being somewhat indigestible and highly expensive, is not commended for daily consumption in the home.

❖*In* Cowboy and Western Songs, *Austin E. and Alta S. Fife write: "We have collected many texts of this song but, unlike most, there is very little variation; it is as if the original song managed to say precisely what was to be said—nothing superfluous, nothing missing. The thesis of the treachery of women is stated, one gripping example thereof is cited, the tragic results are given, and the cowboy's scorn of women is restated with magnified intensity. The whole tragedy rests on an insult to the picture of the girl worshipped by the cowboy, her brash perfidy notwithstanding!"* —R.S.

NO USE FOR THE WOMEN

Collected by Austin and Alta S. Fife   Traditional

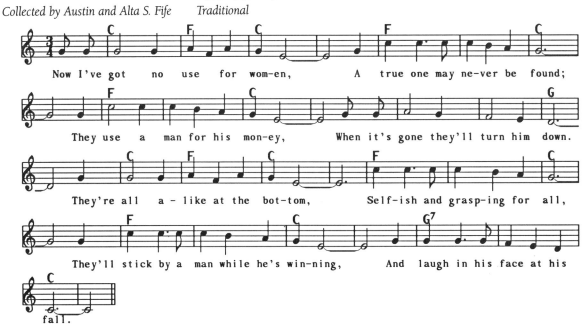

Now I've got no use for wom-en, A true one may ne-ver be found;

They use a man for his mon-ey, When it's gone they'll turn him down.

They're all a-like at the bot-tom, Self-ish and grasp-ing for all,

They'll stick by a man while he's win-ning, And laugh in his face at his

fall.

Cynthia Pease Mann. (Photo courtesy of Idaho State Historical Society)

Now I've got no use for women.
A true one may never be found;
They use a man for his money.
When it's gone they'll turn him down.
They're all alike at the bottom;
Selfish and grasping for all.
They'll stick by a man while he 's winning
And laugh in his face at his fall.

My pal was an honest young puncher,
Honest, upright and true;
But he turned to a hard shooting gunman
On account of a girl named Lou.
He fell in with evil companions,
The kind that are better off dead;
When a gambler insulted her picture
He filled him full of lead.

All through the long night they trailed him,
Through mesquite and thick chaparral;
And I couldn't help think of the woman
As I saw him pitch and fall.
If she'd been the pal that she should have
He might have been raising a son,
Instead of out there on the prairie,
To die by the ranger's gun.

Death's sharp sting did not trouble,
His chances for life were too slim;
But where they were putting his body
Was all that worried him.
He lifted his head on his elbow,
The blood from his wounds flowed red,
He gazed at his pals grouped around him
As he whispered to them and said:

"Oh, bury me out on the prairie,
Where the coyotes may howl o'er my grave;
Bury me out on the prairie,
But from them my bones please save.
Wrap me up in a blanket
And bury me deep in the ground,
Cover me over with boulders
Of granite, gray and round."

So we buried him out on the prairie,
Where the coyotes can howl o'er his grave,
And his soul is now a-resting
From the unkind cut she gave.
And many another young puncher
As he rides past the piles of stones,
Recalls some similar woman
And envies his moldering bones.

❖ *Johnny Carrey reports that Idaho Jack Treadwell wrote this song in Round Valley during the winter of* 1927-1928 *as an answer to the popular song, "I've Got No Use For the Women." It is sung to the same tune.*
—R.S.

I'LL ALWAYS STAND UP FOR THE WOMEN
By Idaho Jack Treadwell

I'll always stand up for the women
Though they say they are the mother of sin.
'Tis only a false accusation—
A willful invention of men.
He was only a four-flushing gambler
Who went broke at his own game
And laid it on to a woman
That she might bear the blame.

My pal was an every-day woman,
Honest, upright, and square.
Her face was seamed and furrowed
And crowned with silvery hair.
All was righteous she taught me;
She led the straight, narrow way—
It wasn't the fault of the woman
That my feet went astray.

All through my childhood she nursed me
With kind, loving patience and care;
And I can but think of that woman
As I breathe my evening prayer.
Year after year she grew feeble
And at last there came the sad day
When her duty here on earth was finished
And she was called away.

But the cold hand of Death did not still her
As she lay on her dying bed;
She smiled at her brood grouped about her
And whispered to them and said;
"Bury me out in the Churchyard
Where the flowers may bloom o'er my grave.
Bury me out in the Churchyard—
'Tis the one mortal wish that I crave."

For a moment her voice grew silent . . .
We looked and the woman was dead.
But into the hands of her Maker
Her immortal spirit had fled.
We buried her out in the Churchyard
Where the flowers still bloom o'er her grave—
But she wears a bright crown up in heaven
For the kind, loving touch that she gave.

Since then I have found it rough travelling
For the road there ceased to be paved
That leads me on this short journey
From the cradle to the grave.
I know that I'm a rambling Rounder
And I know that I am none of the best—
*But it wasn't the fault of the woman
Who nursed me at the breast!*

DON'T LISTEN TO FABLE AND FICTION
'Tis only debauchery and shame!
REMEMBER YOUR MOTHER WAS A WOMAN
SO HONOR AND REVERENCE THE NAME!

Nez Perce woman and child. (Photo courtesy of Idaho State Historical Society)

❖ *Blanche Cowger gave us this song, but I also learned this from my Grandmother Kelly. From the oldest traditional songs to the most contemporary stories, older women have warned young girls to keep away from gypsies and gamblers—and in all that time the warnings have been about as effective as trying to stop the rain.*

—R.S.

THE GYPSY'S WARNING

As Sung by Blanche Cowger

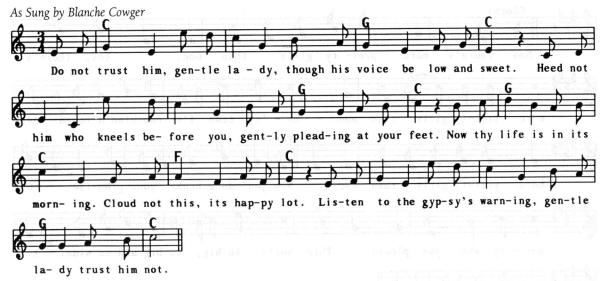

Do not trust him, gen-tle la - dy, though his voice be low and sweet. Heed not him who kneels be- fore you, gent-ly plead-ing at your feet. Now thy life is in its morn- ing. Cloud not this, its hap-py lot. Lis-ten to the gyp-sy's warn-ing, gen-tle la- dy trust him not.

Do not trust him, gentle lady,
Though his voice be low and sweet.
Heed not him who kneels before you,
Gently pleading at your feet.
Now thy life is in its morning.
Cloud not this, its happy lot.
Listen to the gypsy's warning,
Gentle lady, trust him not.

Do not turn so coldly from me.
I would only guard thy youth
From his stern and withering power.
I would only tell thee truth.
I would shield thee from all danger,
Save thee from a tempter's snare.
Listen to the gypsy's warning,
I have warned thee, now beware.

Lady, once there lived a maiden,
Pure and bright and like thee, fair.
But he wooed, wooed and won her,
Filled her gentle heart with care.
Then he heeded not her weeping,
Nor cared he her life to save.
Soon she perished, she is sleeping
In the cold and silent grave.

Keep thy gold, I do not crave it.
Lady, I have prayed for this.
For the hour that I might foil him,
Rob him of expected kiss.
Gentle lady, do not wonder
At my words so cold and wild.
Lady, in the green grave yonder
Lies the gypsy's only child.

❖ *Anna Marie Boles, who grew up in Rock Creek,*
Idaho, tells us that her brothers sang this song. —R.S.

MORE PRETTY GIRLS THAN ONE

As Sung by Anna Marie Boles

Chorus
Now there's more pret-ty girls than one. Yes, there's
more pret-ty girls than one. Ev - 'ry town I've ram-bled a-round seen
more pret-ty girls than one. **Verse** Now you done broke your prom-ise. Go
mar - ry who you please. This world so big, so big and so wide, I'll
ram-ble back some day.

Now, there's more pretty girls than one.
Yes, there's more pretty girls than one.
Every town I've rambled around
Seen more pretty girls than one.

Now you done broke your promise.
Go marry who you please.
This world so big—so big and so wide.
I'll ramble back some day.

Repeat refrain

178

❖ *Little Mohea is the ideal subject of a cowboy's romantic dalliance—eager to please, dark, exotic, foreign, sweet-natured, helpful, and above all, never argumentative when it comes time for him to abandon her and go home and marry someone of his own kind who is pure, white, above reproach, and looks like Grace Kelly. Unfortunately we do not have the music for this particular song.*

—R.S.

LITTLE MOHEA
(As Sung by Blanche Cowger)

As I was out walking for pleasure one day,
Or to seek recreation, I scarcely can say,
As I was amusing myself in the shade
Who chanced to come by me but a fair Indian maid.

She sat down beside me, and taking my hand,
Said, "You look like a stranger, not one of my band.
But if you are willing you're welcome to come,
And share with myself a snug little home."

Together we wandered, together we roamed,
Till we came to a log hut in a coconut grove.
As we came to the log hut she turned unto me,
Saying, "Go no more roaming far across the blue sea."
Saying, "Go no more roving but stay here with me,
And I'll teach you the language of the little Mohea."

"Oh, no, my fair maiden, that never could be
For I have my own true love far across the blue sea.
And if I bereave her, why lonely she'd be,
For her heart beats as truly as the little Mohea."

Oh, now I've safe landed on my own native shore,
My friends and companions all around me once more.
I look all about me but none do I see
With lips to compare with the little Mohea.
I look all about me but none do I see
With lips to compare with the little Mohea.

❖ *Jealous lover ballads from "The Banks of the Ohio" to "Down in the Willow Garden" usually end badly for the female person involved. The plot is always the same—the young man and young woman go to some lonely spot and she either announces that she is leaving him or that he must marry her. In either case he stabs her with a wee pen knife, strangles her, shoots her, beats her about the head and ears with a two-by-four or drags her around by the hair and chucks her into the deep water that flows through the land. The surprise ending in this version, which I have collected many times in the West, from California to Idaho, is indicative of the independent spirit of western women and probably explains why Anthony Trollope had such reservations about falling in love with them. This specific song I first got from Dora Lawrence of Nampa.*

—R.S.

JUANITA

As Sung by Dora Lawrence

"My Juan-i-ta I must leave you. Now's the time to say fare-well."

They were stand-ing 'mid the ru-ins where the am-ber sha-dows fell.

"You will miss me, O Juan-i-ta, but I beg you don't for-get.

In your eyes the tear-drops glis-ten, Juan-i-ta, your eyes are wet.

"My Juanita, I must leave you . . .
　Now's the time to say 'farewell.'"
They were standing 'mid the ruins,
　Where the amber shadows fell.

"You will miss me, Oh Juanita . . .
　But I beg you don't forget . . .
In your eyes the teardrops glisten,
　Juanita, your eyes are wet.

"What, crying. Why, my brave Juanita,
　Do not grieve because I go . . .
I'm not worthy, that's a good girl . . ."
　"But, señor, I love you so . . ."

"Love me . . . Why of course, Juanita . . .
　And I love you, do not grieve . . ."
"But, señor, if you loved me,
　You would never, never leave."

"I did not think that my flirtation
　Would leave such an impress on your heart . . .
Now I go to wed a maiden
　Of my own country, we must part.

"Don't be angry, Dulcinea . . .
　How your cheeks like roses glow . . .
And your dark eyes flash like jewels . . .
　Fairest maid of Mexico!

"One more kiss I'll give you, Dulcy . . ."
　'Round her waist his arms entwined . . .
They were standing 'mid the ruins . . .
　Almost hid by clustering vines.

They have parted now forever . . .
　Juanita leaves the place alone.
In her eyes no teardrops glisten . . .
　From her heart the love has flown.

Next morning, two vaqueros
　Chanced to rest there in the shade . . .
In the evening sought the shelter . . .
　Shelter that the foliage made.

"Por Dios!" cried un vaquero
　As he pulled the vines apart . . .
"Here lies un Americano . . .
　With a dagger in his heart."

❖*At the cowboy poetry gathering in Elko, Nevada, I heard many women's poems reminding the assembled company of the monumental strength and perseverance it takes to keep a ranch household together . . . that goes for any household. As Hannah Arendt says in* The Human Condition: *"The daily fight in which the human body is engaged to keep the world clean and prevent its decay bears little resemblance to heroic deeds. The endurance it needs to repair everyday anew the waste of yesterday is not courage and what makes the effort painful is not danger, but its relentless repetition." I found this poem contributed by Mrs. Fern Larsen in the* Stanley Basin and Sawtooth Valley Cookbook *(1979).* —R.S.

THE WORLD'S HEROINE
By Alice M. Jones

The world is always praising
    All the great folks of the time —
The poets and musicians, and
    The ministers sublime;
But to earth's greatest heroine
    They never cast a look;
I'll tell you who she is at once —
    The blessed household cook.

We hear a lot of lauding for
    The man who goes to war,
The artist and the sculptor, for
    The poet and his lore,
The lawyer and inventor, and
    The author's famous book;
But we never hear a word about
    The blessed household cook.

She saves the lives of thousands
    By her duties every day,
Though she does it in a simple
    And unnoticed quiet way.
But when I am an author,
    I shall surely write a book
About the queen of womankind, —
    The worthy household cook.

Camping at Elk River, ca. 1918. (Photo courtesy of Idaho State Historical Society)

❖ *"Don't You Marry the Mormon Boys" was sung for us all over the state. This version was recorded in Rexburg and it closely resembles the one included in many collections, including the Fife's. There are many localized verses strung out across the country by the pioneers. In Corvallis, Oregon, it's sung as "Don't You Marry the Corvallis Boys"; in Texas, they sing, "Don't Marry the Johnson Boys"; and in Kansas, they sang it this way:* Come all you young girls,

Pay attention to my noise,
Don't fall in love
With the Kansas Boys.
For if you do your part in it,
I know just how 'twill be—
Johnny cake and antelope
Is all you will see.

—R.S.

DON'T MARRY THE MORMON BOYS

Collected by Austin and Alta S. Fife · *Traditional*

Come girls, come, and lis-ten to my noise. Don't you mar-ry the Mor-mon boys.

If you do your for-tune it will be John-ny cakes 'n ba-bies is

all you'll see.

CHORUS:
Come girls, come and listen to my noise
Don't you marry those Mormon boys
If you do, your fortune, it will be
Johnnie Cake and babies is all you'll see.

Verse:
When they go a-preachin', let me tell you what they wear
An old fur coat all picked and bare
An old straw hat, more brim that crown
A pair of dirty socks they've worn the winter round.

CHORUS:

Verse:
Buy a little house and put it on a hill
Make you work against your will
Buy a little cow and milk it with a gourd
Put it in a corner and cover it with a board.
CHORUS:

Most women who sing this change the genders around.
       — Blanche Cowger
       Kooskia, Idaho

I WISH I WAS SINGLE AGAIN

When I was single, oh then, oh then,
When I was single, oh then,
When I was single, my pockets did jingle
And I wish I was single again.

I married me a wife, oh then, oh then,
I married me a wife, oh then,
I married me a wife and was sad all my life
And I wish I was single again.

My wife, she died, oh then, oh then,
My wife, she died, oh then
My wife, she died, and I laughed till I cried
 To think I was single again.

I married another, oh then, oh then,
I married another, oh then,
I married another,
 and she was the devil's stepmother
And I wish I was single again.

My wife got mad, oh then, oh then,
My wife got mad, oh then,
My wife got mad, and she spent all I had
And I wish I was single again.

She beat me and banged me, oh then, oh then,
She beat me and banged me, oh then,
She beat me and banged me,
 and swore she would hang me
And I wish I was single again.

She got a rope, oh then, oh then,
She got a rope, oh then,
She got a rope and my neck did choke
And I wish I was single again.

The limb it did break, oh then, oh then,
The limb it did break, oh then,
The limb it did break and my neck did escape
And I wish I was single again.

Young men take warning of this, of this,
Young men take warning of this,
Be good to the first for the last is much worse
And you will wish you were single again.

❖*My grandmother and I both sing the song this way.*
 —R.S.

Single girl, single girl
dressed all so fine.
Married girl—married girl.
Goes ragged all the time.
Oh Lord, don't I wish
I was a single girl again?

Single girl—single girl
Eats chicken pie—
Married girl—married girl
She'll eat cornbread or die
And lord, don't I wish
I was a single girl again.

❖ *Lyda Southard was known as Lady Bluebeard. She was imprisoned in 1921 for dispatching her fourth husband with arsenic-flavored apple pie. The first three also died mysteriously and no one knows how much damage she did when she escaped.*

She served 20 years in the Idaho State Penitentiary. My Grandfather Kelly sang this little ditty — he either made it up or brought it home from the market place in Twin Falls.

— R.S.

LYDA SOUTHARD'S FAMOUS APPLE PIE
(To the tune of "Annie Laurie")

Oh Twin Falls' farms are bonnie
In the middle of July,
And 'twas there that Lyda Southard
Baked her famous apple pie.
Her famous apple pie . . .
Which ne'er forgot will be . . .
And for Lyda's deep dish apple pie
I'd lay me down and dee.

She sprinkled it with cinnamon,
A dash of nutmeg too,
And sugared it with arsenic,
A Tasty devil's brew.
That famous apple pie . . .
Which ne'er forgot will be . . .
And for Lyda Southard's apple pie,
Men lay them down to die.

Four times she picked her apples
And put them in a pie.
'Twas just dessert, she murmured,
I never thought they'd die,
I never thought they'd die,
I never thought they'd die,
She was just a country housekeeper
Who never thought they'd die.

Oh Lyda's got her just deserts,
She's in the jailhouse strong.
Her piecrust it was short and sweet,
Her sentence it is long.
Her sentence it is long . . .
Her sentence it is long . . .
Oh Lyda's in the jailhouse now,
Her sentence it is long.

HARDHAT
(from Vardis Fisher's *Idaho Lore*, 1939)

Nineteen men and one woman reached the scene of a gold strike in the Coeur d'Alenes. A tent served as a saloon, the one log house being reserved for the woman. One evening she lifted the flap of the saloon tent and announced that she had shot Hardhat. There was no excitement. The men strolled over and observed that Hardhat was dead all right; he had been too drunkenly amorous, apparently, and had reached the end of his trail. A committee was appointed to serve in the capacity of a coroner. Its report of the circumstances did not mention Hardhat at all; but it did express regret that the cleaning up of the new camp had been left to a lady, and extended thanks to her for a job well done.

STORY OF MAGGIE HALL KNOWN AS MOLLY B'DAM
(Contributed by Opal Brooten at the Wallace Song Swap)

Maggie Hall was born in Dublin, Ireland, on November 26, 1863, and wanting to see the new frontier, she landed in New York City at the age of 20. Her first job as a waitress landed her a wealthy but "ne'er do well" husband by the name of Burden. Her new husband thought the name of Maggie Hall was not distinguished enough for one in his station so he introduced her as Molly Burden.

Shortly thereafter, Burden was disowned by his family for his unsavory life style and the family fortune was no longer available to him. Burden not being inclined to work for a living put Molly on the streets and started her in her new profession — shortly thereafter, Molly left Burden.

Molly's new profession found her in the red light districts from New York City to San Francisco and eventually to the frozen north. Hearing of the fabulous fortune to be had in the gold discovery in Idaho, Molly set forth for the diggins in Murray and Eagle on Pritchard Creek, Idaho.

Molly was known not only as a beautiful harlot but as a ministering angel to the poor and sick wherever she went. Well educated, she could recite Shakespeare with the best. Decked out in her finest silks and satins, she would ride her white steed into bars and down a slug of whiskey without batting an eye. On Sunday, Molly could be found in the front row in church.

When a miner was down on his luck, he could always depend on Molly for enough beans and bacon to get back to his diggings, with a grubstake to keep him going. When he was sick, Molly would pack up supplies and medicines and would sometimes sit for days at a bedside to nurse a fellow human being.

Molly's final resting place is Murray, Idaho. Murray and Eagle were roaring gold camps of 10,000 miners and families in a narrow canyon on Pritchard Creek. Wyatt Earp ran a saloon there. Molly's stable mates—some mentioned in the folk lore of the west—Terrible Edith—Bronco Liz—and the famous Calamity Jane, along with others were residents of old Murray, but even tho living amongst their kind, Molly shone like a diamond because of her kind and noble deeds.

There is a story about Molly that illustrates the strength of her character. While riding her great white horse over the pass in the deep snow to Murray, she saved the life of a freezing young mother and son by wrapping them in her fur coat and then riding on into Murray.

She received a cold welcome from the women of Murray and Eagle and it was they who christened her "Molly Be Damn!

Soon after Molly's arrival, smallpox hit the community. Unchecked the disease killed most of the local Indians, dozens of miners and their families. The Murray townspeople would not go near anyone due to their fear of being contaminated. Molly and her girls cleaned out the largest building in the town and established hospitals to care for the sick and dying. They worked night and day without sleep or pay for three weeks to nurse the afflicted.

Later that winter Molly came down with a lingering illness. The Christian ladies and the doctors did all they could but the fever grew worse day by day. Molly died later that winter.

The town closed their doors on that day, January 17, 1888. Molly was only 35 years old. Over 5,000 people came to her funeral to pay their respects. She is buried in the little cemetery on the slope of the mountain along with the graves of the many miners and families that were wiped out in that terrible epidemic.

"Diamond-Tooth Lil"
(Evelyn Fiala Hildegard),
(Photo courtesy of
Idaho State Historical Society)

LEGEND OF MOLLY B' DAM

Written by Dale Miller

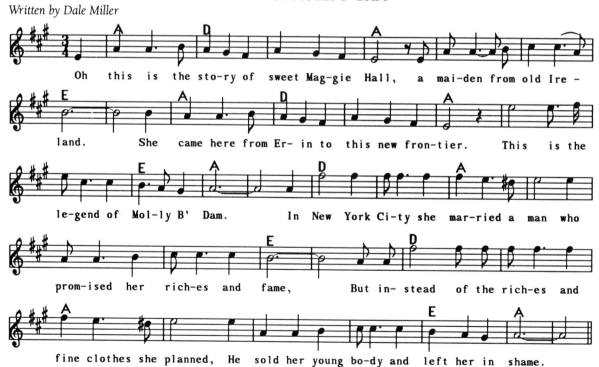

Oh this is the sto-ry of sweet Mag-gie Hall, a mai-den from old Ire-land. She came here from Er-in to this new fron-tier. This is the le-gend of Mol-ly B' Dam. In New York Ci-ty she mar-ried a man who prom-ised her rich-es and fame, But in-stead of the rich-es and fine clothes she planned, He sold her young bo-dy and left her in shame.

186

Oh, this is the story of sweet Maggie Hall,
A maiden from old Ireland.
She came here from Erin to this new frontier.
This is the legend of Molly B'Dam.
In New York City she married a man
Who promised her riches and fame,
But instead of the riches and fine clothes she planned,
He sold her young body and left her in shame.

So Maggie set forth on her journey in life
In the only profession she knew,
But the gold that she garnered in that house of sin
She gave to the sick and the poor that she knew.
Then word came to Maggie that gold had been found
In a canyon in North Idaho.
She boarded a train and left the bright lights
And headed for Murray in the deep winter snow.

On thirty miles on a high mountain pass
She nursed a young mother and son
She kept them from freezing that cold winter night
Then road into Murray her long journey done.
At the old Murray Courthouse a crowd gathered there,
As Maggie road up to the clan
She said my name's Maggie — I'm stayin' awhile
They there christened her Molly B'Dam.

She said, "I'll be stayin' on Gold Street alone
The first cabin there in the row.
There'll be a red lantern a-hangin' in front
For those with the urging and them with the dough!"
But right from the start the word came to town
A miner was sick on his claim.
She packed up and rode back into the hills
And nursed the sick miner with nothing to gain.

Then smallpox invaded that wild mountain town.
Dozens were dying each day.
Her girls and Molly took over the town.
For three weeks they labored without sleep or pay.
Then Molly took sick, it was late in the fall
Her fever grew worse day by day.
The ministers, townsmen, and doctors all tried
But later that winter the girl passed away.

The Murray newspaper was bordered in black
The town closed its doors on that day.
Five thousand were gathered to wish her farewell
And mourned as they laid their sweet Molly away.
So this is the story of sweet Maggie Hall
But the story did not end that day.
It's one hundred years since poor Molly died
They still tend the flowers that grow on her grave.

This is the legend of Molly B'Dam!

An Idahoan, now prominent, tells of prospecting one day in the mountains near Bonanza. He stopped in his tracks by the sight of four beautiful pine trees, off by themselves, and enclosing a square of earth. Then he learned that, long ago, Anna King had been murdered in a dance-hall brawl. The townspeople decided that inasmuch as she had lived "differently" she should be buried "differently." In any case, she was not fit to rest with respectable persons in the cemetery. Some miners from Custer, hearing of the matter, came over and buried the girl. Today the local cemetery, containing the bones of the respectable, is a barren and desolate spot. Anna's grave is framed by four magnificent trees. It is known as the Anna King Hill cemetery, and is cared for by the Department of Forestry.

❖❖❖

❖ *A song purportedly written for and about Rose Morgan who unknowingly married an outlaw, a compatriot of Butch Cassidy, who chanced to take up residence in Star Valley one hard winter to avoid the various posses tracking him. Sung by Julie Glenn at the Rexburg Song Swap. She learned it when she was a child from her sister. Unfortunately we are unable to locate the music for this version.* —R.S.

STAR VALLEY ROSE

Way out in old Star Valley, 'twas many years ago,
Dwelt a lovely sweet Rose Garden, the sweetest girl I know.

One day she met a stranger, a reckless, wandering man
Who said, "I am a rancher," disprove it if you can.

He courted her all winter and bought a wedding ring
And said, "We will be leaving right early in the spring."

And when the snow had melted, and flowers bloomed again,
He took her up to Jackson, to fool the sheriff men.

One day he said, "Rose, darling, you are a robber's wife,
Dear, I am a bandit and hunted for my life."

Eight years Rose lived with William. Each day was filled with fear
The sheriff might come riding and take away her dear.

One day the search was ended, And it will never fail.
They came and took her darling and locked him up in a jail.

Now Rose is sad and lonely, with her living breath
She prays the Lord in heaven to call her home in death.

Now maidens, please remember, be careful as you can.
Don't ever wed a stranger, a reckless wandering man.

❖ *Most versions of this song are unprintable. This one is a cleaned-up parlor song suitable for young ladies with guitars to sing in polite company. That's how my grandfather Kelly got away with singing it in front of my Grandmother Sue. It is often attributed to the outlaw queen — Belle Star.*

—R.S.

MY LOVE IS A RIDER

As Sung by Rosalie Sorrels   Traditional

My love is a rider, wild bron-cos he breaks_____ But he's prom-ised to give it up just for my sake Say, he ties up one foot and the sad-dle puts on_____ with a swing and a jump he is mount - ed and gone _____.

My love is a rider, wild broncos he breaks . . .
But he's promised to give it up just for my sake . . .
Say, he ties up one foot and the saddle puts on . . .
With a swing and a jump he is mounted and gone.

The first time I seen him, it was early in May . . .
I give him a smile as he went on his way . . .
He tipped me a wink as he gaily did go . . .
For he wished me to look at the buckin' bronco.

The next time I seen him, it was late in the fall . . .
Swingin' all the girls around at the ball.
Oh, he laughed and he talked as we danced to and fro'
He said he never would ride on another bronco.

He give me some presents, among them a ring . . .
The return that I give him was a far better thing . . .
'Twas a young maiden's heart and I'd have you all know
That he won it by ridin' on the bucking bronco.

Come all you young maidens where'er you reside . . .
Don't give him your affections if he swings a rawhide . . .
For he'll court you and pet you and leave you and go
In the spring, down the trail, on the buckin' bronco.

❖ *This item Edna McGowan contributed to the* Stanley Basin and Sawtooth Valley Cookbook *(1979), where I found it and "A Grandmother's 'Receet' for Washing Clothes."*
  —R.S.

THE FIVE BEST BOOKS

The Bible

 The Pocket Book

  The Bank Book

   The Check Book

    THE COOK BOOK.

A GRANDMOTHER'S "RECEET" FOR WASHING CLOTHES

1. Bild fire in back yard to het kettle of rain water.

2. Set tubs so smoke won't blow in your eyes if the wind is peart.

3. Shave one hole cake of lie sope into bilin water.

4. Sort things out to make 3 piles: 1 pile white, 1 pile cullord and 1 pile for werk britches and rags.

5. Stur flour into cold water, smooth, then thin down with bilin water.

6. Rub dirty spots on board, scrub hard, then bile. Rub cullord, but don't bile; just rench and starch.

7. Take white things out of kettle with broomstick handel, then rench, blew, and starch.

8. Spred your tee towels on the grass to dry.

9. Hang your old rags on the fence to air.

10. Pore the rench water into your flower beds.

11. Scrub your porch with the hot sopy water.

12. Turn the tubs upside down to drain.

13. Go put on a clean dress, smooth your hair with side combs, then brew up a cup of tee. Set and rest and rock a spell and count your blessins.

Cowgirl on Weiser's State Street. (Photo courtesy of Idaho State Historical Society)

ROUND AND ROUND SHE GOES: THE BARREL RACER
By S. LaPrade Riddel

On a cold Montana morning
   On the road to Idaho
I watched her order hot and black to go.
Don her boots and spurs and bluejeans
   And the lonely in her eyes
Told me just how much she loved the rodeos.

I asked where she was headin',
   She said, the Boise show.
   She took a third in Butte just yesterday.
No, she never has been married,
   And she probably never will,
   'Cause silver buckle dreams
   Don't leave time for standing still.

CHORUS:
Round and Round and Round she goes
Where she stops nobody knows.
The miles are gettin longer,
   And the nights they never end.
Old rodeos and livestock shows
   Keep the lady on the go.
Lord, she loves to run those barrels,
   And its the only life she knows.

For nigh on fifteen seasons
   This circuit's been her home,
   And at times she misses kids she never had.
But she wouldn't trade a minute
   Of the years that she's got in it,
'Cause she's had herself some happy,
   And she's learned to take the sad.

When I looked up from my coffee
   I saw Boise on her mind,
   And she had that look of leavin' in her eyes.
As she drove into the morning
   It slowly dawned on me
How hard it is to tell a dream goodbye
   (You just can't tell a life-long dream good-bye.)

      —S. LaPrade Riddel,
      Pointed Star Music,
      recorded by Chris LeDoux.

191

John L. Woodworth, ca. 1902-03. (Photo courtesy of Idaho State Historical Society)

I'M GONNA TELL

SONGS FOR GROWN-UP KIDS & CHILDREN

I'm gonna tell that you busted the plate
I'm gonna tell bout the bananas you ate
I'll tell on you one time, I'll tell on you two
I'm gonna tell on you.

Rosalie Sorrels

Telling — either tattling or relating stories, tall tales, lies, flights of fancy — is the business of a child. Grown-up story-tellers are all children in disguise. If you want to gain the trust of a child, you'll learn to tell. Trust me — I have spent my life resisting the process of growing up.   —R.S.

I'm gonna tell, I'm gonna tell
I'm gonna holler and I'm gonna yell
I'll get you in trouble for everything you do
I'm gonna tell on you.

I'm gonna tell that you've hid the broom
So you wouldn't have to sweep up your room
Then mamma will sweep the room up with you
I'm gonna tell on you.

I'm gonna tell that you busted the plate
I'll tell about the bananas you ate
I'll tell on you one time, I'll tell on you two
I'm gonna tell on you.

I'm gonna tell that you kicked me and you hit me
I'm gonna tell that you punched me and you bit me
But I won't tell mamma what I did to you
I'm just gonna tell on you.

193

Mom wrote this song after we moved back to Boise. I remember she was working around the house and was getting so frustrated with us kids, cause we kept coming up telling on each other. She just sat down and started to sing. I remember getting so mad I wanted to punch her cause she wouldn't do anything except sing that song.

— Holly Sorrels Marizu

I'M GONNA TELL

Written by Rosalie Sorrels, Grimes Creek Music ASCAP *Music by Rosalie Sorrels*

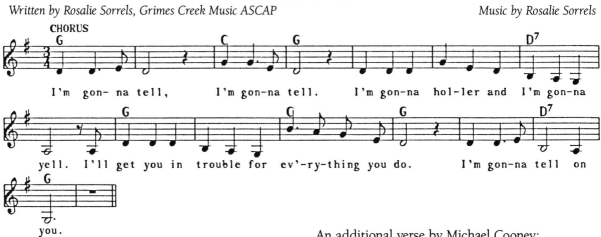

I'm gon-na tell, I'm gon-na tell. I'm gon-na hol-ler and I'm gon-na yell. I'll get you in trouble for ev'-ry-thing you do. I'm gon-na tell on you.

An additional verse by Michael Cooney:

I'm gonna tell daddy that you suck your thumb
I'm gonna tell what you did with your gum
and soon he'll find out about the cat and the glue
and I'm gonna tell on you

❖ *I first learned this song from Dora Lawrence of Nampa, Idaho. It seems to be very well known — I've heard it from several people since Mrs. Lawrence first sang it to me. I'd say it probably came from old time traveling entertainments much like Chautauqua tent shows, or early vaudeville.*

—R.S.

MR. DOONDERBECK

As Sung by Dora Lawrence *Traditional*

There was a good old Ger-man man, His name was Doon-der-beck He was ver-y fond of poo-dle dogs, Sau-er-kraut and speck. He owned a great big but-cher shop, the fin-est e-ver seen. He got him out a pa-tent to make

194

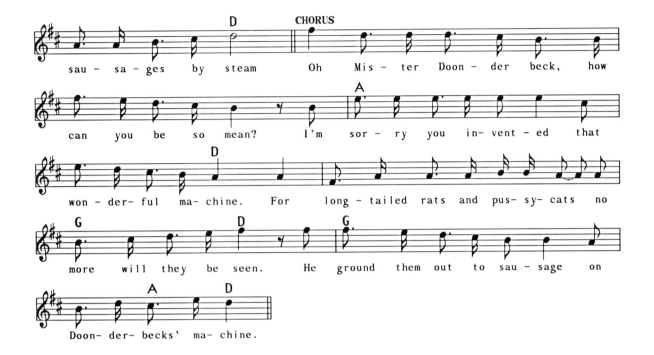

There was a good old German man, his name was Doonderbeck.
He was very fond of poodle dogs, sauerkraut, and speck.
He owned a great big butcher shop, the finest ever seen.
He got him out one patent, to make sausages by steam.

CHORUS:
Oh, Mr. Doonderbeck, how can you be so mean?
I'm sorry you invented that wonderful machine.
For the long tailed rats and pussy cats no more will they be
    seen.
He ground them out to sausage on Doonderbeck's machine.

The other day a little boy he stepped into the store
To buy a pound of sausage that was walking round the floor
And while he was standing there, he whistled out the tune
That made the sausages start to hop and jump around the room.

CHORUS:
Now something got the matter, that machine it wouldn't go.
So Doonderbeck, he crawled inside for to find it out you know.
His wife, she took a nightmare while walking in her sleep.
She gave that crank one terrible yank and Doonderbeck was meat.

I learned this song from Paul Croy who learned it from his father, who came from Ohio. They used to sing it as a family with Paul's mother accompanying on the piano. I've taught it to school kids in and around Hope, who enjoy accelerating after every verse.

— Joan Brounstein (Hope)

HERRO JERRO

As Sung by Paul Croy

When I was young I lived in the woods
Tudda ring tum bonny mitcha kymo
I had a pair of oxen but they weren't any good
Tudda ring tum bonny mitcha kymo

CHORUS:
Herro jerro kymo kemo
Here come a lapstrap
Penny winkle fummydiddle
Yellow bubble ring tum
Bonny mitcha kymo.

I traded my oxen for a cow
Tudda ring tum bonny mitcha kymo
She tried to give milk but she didn't know how
Tudda ring tum bonny mitcha kymo.

I traded my cow for a calf
Tudda ring tum Bonny mitcha kymo
Every time I traded I lost just half
Tudda ring tum bonny mitcha kymo.

I traded my calf for a goat
Tudda ring tum bonny mitcha kymo
He ate a bar of soap, got a bubble in his throat
Tudda ring tum bonny mitcha kymo.

I traded my goat for a dog . . .
He never learned to bark
but he slept like a log . . .

I traded my dog for a cat . . .
She clawed up all the curtains
but she couldn't catch a rat . . .

I traded my cat for a goose . . .
I closed the gate but still he got loose . . .
Saddle and bridle on the shelf . . .
If you want any more please sing it to yourself . . .

This is a parody that I picked up at a family reunion. Anyway, it was on my husband's side of the family, one or the other. It's a parody of "In the Shade of the Old Apple Tree" and it's called "Neath the Crust of the Old Apple Pie."

— Linda Crofts (Burley)

'NEATH THE CRUST OF THE OLD APPLE PIE
(To the Tune of
"In the Shade of the Old Apple Tree")

Neath of the crust of the old apple pie
There is something for you and for I
It may be a pin that the cook just dropped in
Or it may be a dear little fly
Or it may be an old rusty nail
Or a piece of a pussy cat's tail
But whatever it be
It's for you and for me
Neath the crust of the old apple pie.

I remember my Grandma and Grandpa Smith (at their farm near Thornton) singing this song forever in my life. I don't think I ever didn't know it. When I was in my early twenties, I was singing this song to some small children who were related to my friend Carol Throop Thompson in Los Angeles. After I finished the English version, Carol sang it in French and told me she had learned it from a relative from France. I haven't traced it further than that, but I suppose it's an old children's song from Europe.

— Virginia DeFoggi (Pocatello)

SHEPHERD MAIDEN

There was a shepherd maiden,
Sing hey a ding dong, a ding a ring dong,
There was a shepherd maiden
Kept sheep upon the hill, ding dong
Kept sheep upon the hill.

She made a cheese so tiny,
Sing hang a ding dong, a ding a ring dong,
She made a cheese so tiny
And sang her little song, ding dong . . .
And sang her little song.

The cat beside the window
With roguish air looked on . . .

Now puss, you must not touch it . . .
Or you must go along.

With paws he did not touch it . . .
But with his whiskers long . . .

So drive away the kitty . . .
Because he was so wrong.

ON TOP OF THE SCHOOL HOUSE
(Sung to the tune of "On Top of Old Smokey")

A Ape. a   B Bear. b

C Cock. c   D Dog. d

E Elephant. e   F Fox. f

On top of the school house
All covered with sand,
I shot Mrs. Butler
With a red rubber band.

I shot her with pleasure,
I shot her with pride . . .
How could I miss her?
She's a hundred feet wide.

I went to her funeral,
I went to her grave,
Instead of red roses.
I threw a grenade.

I looked in her coffin,
She wasn't quite dead,
So I took a bazooka
And blew off her head.

G Goose. g   H Horse h

MINE EYES HAVE SEEN THE GLORIES
(To the Tune of
"The Battle Hymn of the Republic")

Mine eyes have seen the glories of the burning of the schools
We have tortured all the teachers and we're breaking
   all the rules —
We are marching 'round the playground and we'll burn
   the principal —
March on 2nd grade — march on!

CHORUS:
Glory, glory Hallelujah —
Teacher hit me with a ruler!
Hit him in the bean
With a rotten tangerine
March on 2nd grade, march on!

J Ibex i

As far back as I can remember, my grandmother, Mrs. Evva Smith Derricott, and her twin sister, Mrs. Eva Smith Parker, would always sing it right after the family dinner and as a prelude to the rest of the family program of music, readings, and such.

— Delmar S. Derricott (Preston)

THAT LITTLE SHIRT THAT MOTHER MADE FOR ME

As Sung by Delmar Derricott

I can't forget the day that I was born:
'Twas on a cold and frosty winter's morn.
The doctor said I was a chubby chap,
Then the nurse she took me on her lap.
Oh, she bathed me all over I remember,
And after powder puffing me you see,
She put me in the cradle by the window
In that little shirt that Mother made for me.

The first day that I wore my knickerbocks,
It seemed so funny after wearing frocks.
I was a little picture they did say,
When they let me out to run and play.
Oh, I didn't like the pants that I was wearing
So in the street I took them off you see,
And started walking home so brave and daring,
In that little shirt that Mother made for me.

And then to school they said that I must go.
I never liked my teacher you must know,
And when I played the truant quite so dear,
Teacher said, "Now, Delmar, you come here."
With a big stick she beat around, upon me.
There's no mistake about my pedigree
I had the map of Scotland printed on me,
'Neath that little shirt that Mother made for me.

THE PHILADELPHIA LAWYER

As Sung by Dick Person

Written by Woody Guthrie

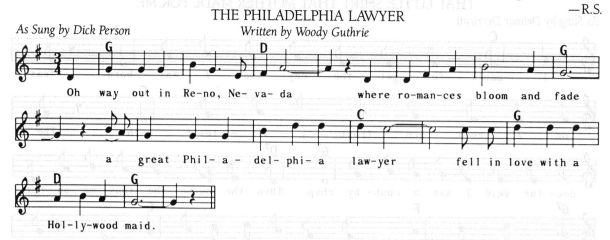

Oh way out in Re-no, Ne-va-da where ro-man-ces bloom and fade a great Phil-a-del-phi-a law-yer fell in love with a Hol-ly-wood maid.

Oh, way out in Reno, Nevada,
Where romances bloom and fade,
A great Philadelphia lawyer
Fell in love with a Hollywood maid.

Oh, come, love, and we will wander
Down where the lights are so bright;
I'll win you a divorce from your husband
And we can get married tonight.

Wild Bill was a gun-totin' cowboy,
Six notches were carved on his gun;
And all the boys around Reno
Left Wild Bill's maiden alone.

One night when Bill was returning
Out from the desert so cold,
He dreamed of his Hollywood sweetheart . . .
Her love was as lasting as gold.

Well, Bill looked up in the moonlight,
Two shadows he saw on the shade;
'Twas the great Philadelphia lawyer
Making love to his Hollywood maid.

Oh, your hands are so soft and so lovely,
Your form is so rare and divine;
Come away with me to the city
And leave this wild cowboy behind.

Well, way back in old Pennsylvania,
The stars they are shining so bright,
But there's one less Philadelphia lawyer
In old Pennsylvania tonight.

Everyone in Idaho has heard the legend of Bigfoot. I included Tony Taylor's "Ballad of Starr Wilkinson," which can be sung as a dirge. Many stories were told about the giant size of the famous Indian desperado Starr Wilkinson, also known as Bigfoot, who roamed southern Idaho between Boise and Silver City. The following description is from Idaho Lore. —R.S.

Even though legend has doubtless exaggerated his size, given him feet seventeen inches long, a chest as big as a barrel, and a speed afoot almost equal to that of a horse, it is known that he was an enormous man with feet so large that their imprint betrayed him everywhere he went. It is said that three men once set out on fast horses to run him down and pursued him for thirty miles in one day and could not overtake him . . . .

Bigfoot's favorite field of slaughter lay between Boise and Silver City, and especially in a narrow defile a few miles south of Snake River. Here with his band of rascals he waited and one by one picked off the early settlers traveling between the two towns. He was a terror and a scourge; but he was also a most cunning villain who outwitted all attempts to capture him. In July of 1868 he met his man . . . .His name was J.W. Wheeler. He was a jolly merry maker who gave gusto to any crowd in which he found himself; and he was, rumor declared, a dead shot . . . . Without moving from where he stood, and with extra-ordinary coolness, Wheeler kept firing as the great fellow raced toward him. When thirty yards away, Bigfoot went down with a broken leg, never to rise again. . . . According to John's report, Bigfoot now told his story: that his father was a white man, Archer Wilkinson, who had hanged for murder; that his mother was part Cherokee, part Negro. He himself had been named Starr for Thomas Starr, a desperado. In the Cherokee Nation he had loved a girl, but in an emigrant train en route to the West, she fell in love with an artist, whereupon Bigfoot choked the man to death and threw him into the Snake River. He named the persons whom he had murdered, and then he died. It is said his death long remained a mystery because of Wheeler's promise not to reveal it.

— Vardis Fisher
(*Idaho Lore*, 1939)

THE BALLAD OF STARR WILKINSON 1868
By Tony Taylor

My name it is Starr Wilkinson! Don't doubt my dying words!
No matter what they call me or what you may of heard . . . .
You see I'm mostly Whiteman and that's the part I hate
and I killed that two-faced woman where the Boise meets the Snake.

My mother was a Christian, Cherokee and Black,
my father hung for murder without an inch of slack.
I left the "reservation" to make a better stand
and took the Road to Oregon to find the "Promised Land."

It was near the Goose Creek Mountains where the murky waters flow,
that I killed my only chances and slew her New York beau.
Since I've killed me plenty and some women you can bet,
but had twelve slugs not caught me, I'd be killing out there yet.

You shot my wife and baby; you know you done me wrong,
but I was mad and foolish and a badman I belong.
You see I'm mostly Whiteman and that's the part I hate
and I killed that two-faced woman where the Boise meets the Snake.

This desert is my homeland, the only one I claim,
and even though I'm dying, please don't forget my name!
Lay me in the willows with my Henrys by my side,
heap the rocks atop me and mark not when you ride . . . .
You see I'm mostly Whiteman and that's the part I hate
as I cross that darkened water where the Boise meets the Snake.

This ballad comes to us from Australia, where, next to "Waltzing Matilda," it is the most popular of all folksongs. John Greenway believes that this ballad is a generalization of the ballad "Bold Jack Donahue," created when Australian authorities outlawed the singing of the latter ballad after it had become an expression of political protest. If such is the case, then a great deal indeed is known about the hero of this ballad. Donahue was the first of the great Australian outlaws. Transported from Ireland to Australia in 1825, he soon resumed his trade as highwayman. He and his gang avoided capture for two years, but they were finally surrounded by the police at Bringelly, New South Wales, in September, 1830. Donahue was fatally shot in the head, though his companions escaped only to be later captured or killed.

— Kenneth S. Goldstein
(Folk Songs of Idaho and Utah, 1961)

❖*Dora Lawrence, of Nampa, Idaho, gave me this song. She told me that at Halloween she always gave the kids caramel apples and invited them in for hot chocolate. While they were warming up on that cold holiday, she'd sing the "Wild Colonian Boy" and other old songs as her gift to the "trick or treaters."* —R.S.

THE WILD COLONIAN BOY

As Sung by Dora Lawrence   Traditional

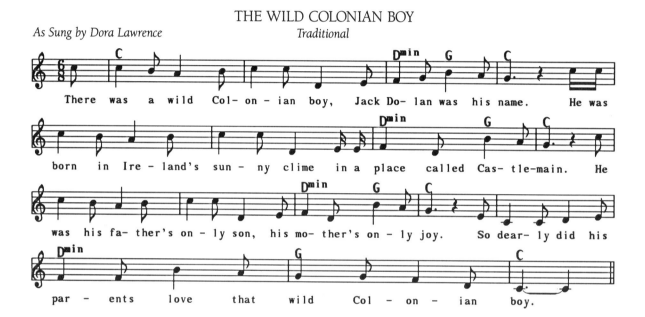

There was a wild colonian boy, Jack Dolan was his name.
He was born in Ireland's sunny clime in a place called
    Castlemain.
He was his father's only son, his mother's only joy.
So dearly did his parents love that wild colonian boy.

'Twas at the age of sixteen years he left his native home,
And to Australia's sunny clime, a bushranger to roam.
And at the age of eighteen years he began his wild career;
He robbed the rich, he helped the poor, he stopped Judge Black
    with joy,
And he trembling gave his gold up to the wild colonian boy.

'Twas on a bright May morning, young Jackie rode along,
A-listening to the mocking birds a-singing their noted song;
Up rode three bold policemen, Kelly, Davis, and Fitzroy,
The three rode out to capture that wild colonian boy.

Surrender, Jack Dolan, you see there's three to one!
Surrender in the Queen's name, you are her plundering son.
He drew a pistol from his side and he waved that little toy;
I'll fight, but I'll not surrender, said the wild colonial boy.

He fired a shot at Kelly, and it brought him to the ground,
But in return from Kelly's gun he received a fatal wound.
A bullet sharp, it pierced his heart, from the pistol of Fitzroy,
And that's the way they captured this wild colonial boy.

❖❖❖

❖ *This is a lovely nonsense song that would tickle any kid. It tickles me! Jackie Brooks (Caldwell) writes that her mother used to sing her this song.* —R.S.

THE CANNIBAL SONG

As Sung by Jackie Brooks

I sent her a pipe with a gold-en cog, a box of tea and a yel-ler dog. I sent her my love with a great big frog a way on the Con-go Is lands. A Hong Kong a hoke a poke a hin-gle a jin-gle a soak a woke a Hong Kong a hoke a bok-ee a way on the Con-go Is-lands.

I sent her a pipe with a golden cog,
A box of tea and a yeller dog.
I sent her my love with a great big frog
Away on the Congo Islands.

Chorus:
Hong Kong a hoke-a-poke
A hingle a jingle a soke-a-woke
A hong kong a hoke-a-bokee
Away on the Congo Islands.

She smoked the pipe with a golden cog,
She drank the tea, she ate the dog.
She returned my love with a great big frog
Away on the Congo Island.

Jackie Fields' family lives in handmade houses in a canyon in the mountains outside Pinehurst. She sang some old songs, but I was particularly struck by the songs she'd made up to use in the community now. As carefully made as the family houses and as organic as the gardens that surround those dwellings, her songs continue the tradition of using what's at hand to get to the heart. *(Photo courtesy of Michael Cordell)*

ABOUT A MILE

As Sung by Jackie Fields ("Honey Won't You Follow Me")

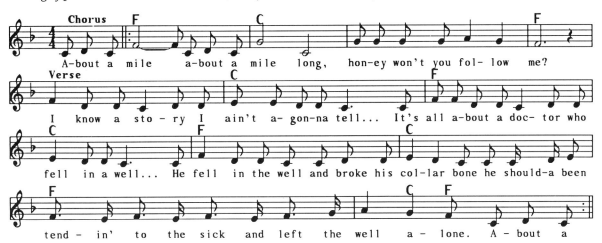

I know a story I ain't a-gonna tell
it's all about a doctor who fell in the well
— he fell in the well and broke his collarbone.
He should'a been tendin to the sick
and left the well alone.

CHORUS:
About a mile, about a mile long
honey won't you follow me.

Pappa took a shave so the story goes,
The razor slipped and it cut off his nose,
The doctor sewed it on, he got it upside down,
and every time it rains Poor Papa nearly drowns.

CHORUS:
I know a girl, she's 8 feet tall.
She sleeps in the kitchen with her feet in the hall,
She's got a sister who lies across the lake,
And she can shake a shimmy like a rattlesnake.

CHORUS:

Hollis and Nadine Murray.(Photo courtesy of Idaho State Historical Society)

205

❖ *This song is sung in every region of the state. My grandmother, Rosalie Cope Stringfellow, used to sing this to me when I was a child. Emma Newgen of Parma says her two older sisters and a brother would ask their mother (who was "from the Ozarks and knew every folk song and ballad") to sing "Babes In The Woods" when they wanted to see her cry.*

Judy Ouderkirk, at the Boise song swap, sang us a slightly different version she learned from "a most dear and precious family friend who sang it to me as an infant and all through my childhood. Cora Howland — who was not really a relative but everyone called her Auntie Corie — lived in a little grapevine-covered yellow house with no electricity or plumbing on the back forty of my Grandpa's farm. The only way back to her house was on the dirt field road. Auntie Corie came to Idaho via covered wagon in the late 1880's. Her mother had died of pneumonia leaving her father to care for eight children. Unable to deal with this he gave his children away to friends. Auntie Corie's new family brought her west."

—R.S.

BABES IN THE WOODS

As Sung by Rosalie Sorrels   Traditional

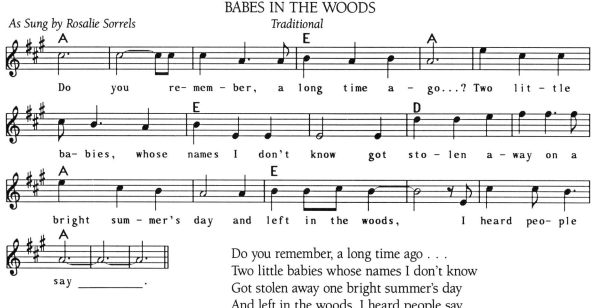

Do you remember, a long time ago...? Two little babies, whose names I don't know got stolen away on a bright summer's day and left in the woods, I heard people say _____.

Do you remember, a long time ago . . .
Two little babies whose names I don't know
Got stolen away one bright summer's day
And left in the woods, I heard people say.

And when it was night, so sad was their plight . . .
The moon went away and the stars gave no light.
They sobbed and they sighed and they bitterly cried,
Then the two little babies laid down and died.

And when they were dead, the robins so red
Brought strawberry leaves and over them spread . . .
And all through the day they sang this sad song . . .
Poor babes in the woods . . . poor babes in the woods.

Repeat first verse . . .

❖*Randy Priest of Boise learned this song from his uncle, Franklin Hess, a railroad man from Pocatello.* *It's one of the best brags I've ever come across.* —R.S.

TRUE BLUE BILL

As Sung by Randy Priest

I was raised in the mountains
Out where the snakes have legs . . .
Where the hoot owls speak in English
And the roosters lay square eggs.
I shaved my beard and moustache
The morning I was born . . .
That night I beat my old man up
And I drank his rye and corn.
CHORUS
Oh, I'm a truthful fellow . . .
They call me True Blue Bill.

I never told a falsehood
And I prob'ly never will.

I used to be a flier
In my aeroplane . . .
Well I flew over to Paris
And I started back again.
When I got halfway over,
The goddamned motor balked,
So I left my plane a-sittin' up there
And I got out and walked.

❖ *Randy Priest (Boise) says this is a "party song" he learned from Vern Bybee in Pocatello.* —R.S.

POOR WILLIE

As Sung by Randy Priest

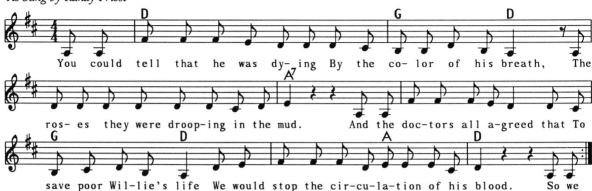

You could tell that he was dy-ing By the co-lor of his breath, The ros-es they were droop-ing in the mud. And the doc-tors all a-greed that To save poor Wil-lie's life We would stop the cir-cu-la-tion of his blood. So we

You could tell that he was dying
By the color of his breath . . . .
The roses, they were drooping in the mud,
And the doctors all agreed that
To save poor Willie's life
We would stop the circulation of his blood.

So we gently dipped his head
In a pot of boiling lead . . .
Laid our darling Willie down to rest.
And the burglars came at night
And they entered without fright
And they stole the mustard plaster from his chest.

Well, I've just come from the barber
To fulfill his last request . . .
To plant a bunch of whiskers on his grave.

❖❖❖

❖ *This is another traditional song from the Bundy Family in Lewiston. I included it here because it blends a number of important elements from the tall tale-quality of the lyrics to the rhythm of their internal rhymes.* —R.S.

RISSITY RASSITY

I married my wife in the month of June
Rissity rassity now now now
I took her home by the light of the moon.
Rissity rassity hage and daffity
Willity wallity rustic in quality
Naggity naggity now now now

She combed her hair just once a year
And every time it brought a tear.

She swept the floor just twice a year
She said that brooms were very dear.

She churned the butter in her dad's old boot
And for a dasher she used her foot.

The butter turned out all grizzaly gray
The cheese took legs and ran away.

The saddle and bridle hang up on the shelf
If you want any more song, go sing it yourself.

If we may judge from its wide incidence in oral songlore, one of the most popular commonplaces in all folksong is the "Who will shoe..." stanzas associated with "The Lass of Roch Royal" (Child #76). It is hardly surprising that the folk have chosen to parody such sacred lines and "My Last Cigar" is but one of the parodies, and perhaps the funniest of all.

—Kenneth S. Goldstein
(Folk Songs of Idaho and Utah, 1961)

❖ I learned this originally from Mrs. Warren Ball in Boise. It is also part of the Bundy family's (Lewiston) repertoire.
—R.S.

MY LAST CIGAR

As Sung by Mrs. Warren Ball

Oh who will smoke my last ci-gar my last ci-gar? Who will smoke my last ci-gar my last ci-gar? Who will smoke my last ci-gar my last ci-gar when I am far a - way--------?

Oh, who will smoke my last cigar, my last cigar?
Who will smoke my last cigar, my last cigar?
Who will smoke my last cigar, my last cigar?
When I am far away?

Oh, I will smoke your last cigar, your last cigar,
I will smoke your last cigar, your last cigar,
Oh, I will smoke your last cigar, your last cigar,
When you are far away.

Oh, who will drink my glass of wine, my glass of wine? (3 times)
When I am far away?

Oh, I will drink your glass of wine, your glass of wine, (3 times)
When you are far away.

Oh, who will feed my little ducks, my little ducks? (3 times)
When I am far away?

Oh, I will feed your little ducks, your little ducks, (3 times)
When you are far away.

Oh, who will kiss my Mary Ann, my Mary Ann? (3 times)
When I am far away?

Oh, I will kiss your Mary Ann, your Mary Ann, (3 times)
When you are far away.

This modern news ballad, just four decades old, details the death of little Kathy Fiscus of San Marino, California. The child, only three years old, was playing with other children when she disappeared on April 8, 1949. A search of the vicinity resulted in her being discovered at the bottom of a long, narrow, abandoned, dry, well-pipe. The child was still able to answer her parent's call when found. Rescue workers struggled around the clock to reach the child. The next day, the child's body was sighted and a doctor was lowered into the well. He was pulled up only to pronounce the child dead.

As in the strikingly parallel case of Floyd Collins, a quarter of a century earlier, songs were quickly composed relating to the story of Kathy Fiscus' death. Indeed, at least seven (and probably more) different songs on the subject were turned into music publishers within a week of the occurrence. The ballad sung here was written and recorded by the late Jimmie Osborne, hillbilly singer and song-writer from Kentucky.

— Kenneth S. Goldstein
(Folk Songs of Idaho and Utah, 1961)

❖ *I learned this version from Dick Person, of Cascade who reportedly learned it from a woman who lived in San Marino at the time the tragedy occurred.*

DEATH OF KATHY FISCUS

As Sung by Dick Person

On A-pril the eighth year for-ty nine Death claimed a lit-tle girl so pure and so kind. Ka-thy, they called her, met her doom that day. I know it was God that called her a-way.

On April the eighth, year forty-nine
Death claimed a little girl so pure and so kind;
Kathy, they called her, met her doom that day.
I know it was God that called her away.

Well, playmates with Kathy were all having fun,
The story it goes they all started to run,
When they looked back, she wasn't there;
It's so hard to think of this tragic affair.

The people they gathered from far and from near,
The workmen they struggled in sadness and fear;
But after two days their hopes grew so weak . . .
They called down to Kathy, but she never did speak.

After working so hard, both day and night,
Digging for hours, she came into sight;
Little darling was dead, her life it was gone;
Now in San Marino there's a heart-broken home.

I know she's an angel in God's sweet abode,
Playing with children in a mansion of gold.
As I stand alone, so humbly I vow,
I know Kathy's happy up there with God now.

THE STRAWBERRY ROAN

As Sung by Lon Baldwin

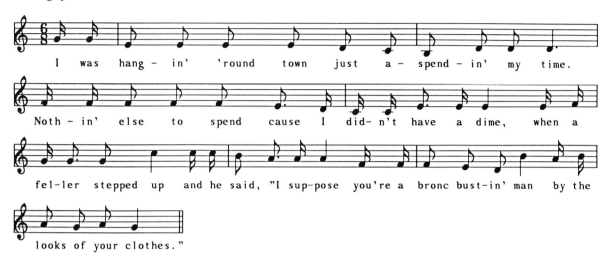

I was hang - in' 'round town just a - spend - in' my time.

Noth - in' else to spend cause I did- n't have a dime, when a

fel-ler stepped up and he said, "I sup-pose you're a bronc bust-in' man by the

looks of your clothes."

I was hangin around town, just a spendin my time,
Nothing else to spend cause I didn't have a dime
When a feller stepped up and he said, "I suppose,
Yer a bronc bustin man, by the looks of yer clothes."
"You guess-ed me right, and a good one," I claimed,
"Do ya happen to have any bad ones to tame?"
He said he had one, a bad one to buck.
At a throwin good riders, he'd had a lot'a luck.
He said the old pony had never been rode,
That the bull that got on him was sure to get
    throwed,
I gets all excited, and I asked what he paid
To ride that ol pony, just a couple of days.
Why the hoss never lived that I couldn' fan,
The horse never lived, he never drew breath,
That I couldn't ride, till he starved plumb to death."
He said, "get yer saddle and I'll give you a chance."
So he gets in the buckboard and rides to the ranch.
I stayed until mornin', and right after chuck,
I stepped out to see if that outlaw can buck,
There in the horse corral standin' alone
Was the old *caballo*, a strawberry roan.
His knees was all spavined, he had pigeon toes,
Little pig eyes and a big Roman nose,
Little pin ears that touch at the tips
With a big forty-four branded on his left hip
A U-neck and old, with a long lower jaw.
You could see with an eye, he's a regular outlaw.

I buckles on my spurs, I'm a sure feelin fine.
I pulled down my old hat and I coiled up my twine,
I piled the loop on him as well I know then
That before he gets rode I'll sure earn my ten.
I gets the blinds on him, it sure is a fight;
Next comes the saddle, I screws her down tight;
Then I gets on him and raises the blinds,
Git out of the way, he's a gonna unwind.
He bends his old neck and I guess he unwound,
Cause he seemed to quit livin down there on the
    ground;
Goes up to east, come down to the west
I stayed with his middle, I's a doin my best.
He sure was frog-walkin, he heaved a big sigh,
And he only lacked wings to be on the fly;
He turned his old belly right up to the sun,
He sure is a sun-fishing son-of-a-gun.
I looses my stirrup, and also my hat.
I'm a-goin' for leather as blind as a bat,
Phenomenal jump he goes up on high
And leaves me a-settin' way up in the sky.
I turned over twice and I come back to earth,
And I lights into cussin the day of his birth.
Well, there's old ponies I ain't able to ride.
There's some of em a livin', they haven't all died,
But I'll bet all my money there's no man alive
. . . can stay with ol' Strawberry when he makes
    that high dive.

211

Blaine Stubblefield, folklorist and founder of the Old Time Fiddlers' Festival in Weiser, Idaho. His respect for folk music and the people who sing it remains an important legacy in Idaho and inspired the public approach taken in this project. (Photograph courtesy of the Weiser Chamber of Commerce and the Old Time Fiddlers Hall of Fame, Weiser, Idaho)

FIDDLIN' AT AN IDAHO DANCE

SWING AND STOMP

Gone is he who made my campfire brighter
As he played for me a lovely fiddle tune?
Gone is he who made my burdens lighter
And made the evening end but all too soon?

Allen C. Rice
(A Tribute to Glenn Manring)

This section is dedicated to the memory of Blaine Stubblefield, who was the first person who ever showed me the value of the attic full of music memories my head had become by the time I met him.

The tradition of oldtime fiddling is strong in Idaho. A dedication in a booklet entitled "The Idaho Oldtime Fiddlers," published in 1963 for Idaho Territorial Centennial, had this to say:

Idaho was full of fiddles and fiddlers. Some were prominent, some almost obscure. They ranged in age from nine to ninety— their talents were varied. Some lived in cities, some far removed from any form of civilization. Many fiddled along in loneliness, being called upon only as occasion demanded—for a small country gathering, a golden wedding celebration or a small town parade.

In 1949, Blaine Stubblefield of Weiser proposed the staging of an old-time fiddlers contest. Fiddling contests had been held in and around the Weiser area prior to World War I. In 1953, the first Fiddlers Festival was presented as an intermission entertainment during the annual square dance festival at Weiser. Later, the square dance festivals were discontinued and the joyous affair that has become the National Oldtime Fiddlers' Festival held every June took over.

Blaine Stubblefield was born January 26, 1896, at Enterprise, Oregon, in the Wallowa Mountains, not far from Hells Canyon. He was brought up amid folk singing and fiddle music. He graduated from the University of Idaho and went to promoting travel on

213

the newly-completed U.S. 95 Highway from Weiser to Lewiston for the Spokane Chamber of Commerce and the American Automobile Association. He was a Lieutenant in the Air Force during World War I and served as an instructor in Texas.

He served as publicity manager for Varney (now United) Airlines in San Francisco and as Washington Editor on Aviation for McGraw-Hill Publications of New York. He attended President Franklin D. Roosevelt's weekly press conferences prior to World War II and spent his leisure time going into the remote areas of the Appalachian Mountains searching out and recording the songs of folk singers for the Library of Congress. In Washington and New York he often hired out as an entertainer, singing his folk songs of which he had made an extensive study.

Blaine Stubblefield died in 1959 but he will long be remembered by those who love fiddling and folk music.

—R.S.

IN MEMORIAM: GONE?

Gone is he who made my campfire brighter
As he played for me a lovely fiddle tune?
Gone is he who made my burdens lighter
And made the evening end but all too soon?

Gone is he who strummed upon his banjo
Or plucked a trembling note on his guitar?
Is this seasoned wood from Heaven? Only he'd know
As he carved a fiddle from a tree a-far.

No, all he gave to me I long shall cherish,
The brilliance of his smile still here it seems;
And the goodness of his life shall never perish
But endure like sunshine, flowers and
     mountain streams.

Yes, my memories of him shall live forever
And the melodies he played will never die;
And his fellowship with man no one can sever
Tho' he plays his instrument for God—on high!
     —Allen C. Rice
     (A Tribute to Glenn Manring)

❖ *My favorite memories of the Weiser Fiddle Contest date back to the Blaine Stubblefield days. There was always a sort of free-for-all warm-up when thirty or so of the best fiddlers would play "Buffalo Gals" center stage. On each side of the proscenium lip would be Fred Haun of Weiser and Fiddling Dave Dummler (of Kansas) accompanying the fiddlers with home-made hammered dulcimers. In all my years of going to folk and bluegrass festivals, I've never heard anything else like that. The other thing I loved was that everyone had to be able to play a waltz as well as a schottische or polka and a "flash" tune: break-down, hoe-down, horn-pipe, or one of those. I could still be moved to tears listening to Almon Maines playing Annie Laurie so sweetly on his hand-made fiddle.* —R.S.

The tune "Whistler's Waltz," I learned from Idaho fiddler Faye Frisbee in Weiser at the fiddle contest in 1962 or 1963. I fell in love with the tune and my mind delivered up a set of words evocative of an affair of the heart some years earlier which no longer bears too close an examination. —Bruce "Utah" Phillips

OLD MEM'RIES OF YOU

Written by Bruce "Utah" Phillips

Darlin', you say that you're goin' away,
For those bright lights your heart always yearns.
You say with a smile you'll be gone just a while
But I know now you'll never return.

CHORUS:
Old mem'ries of you, darlin', see how they fly . . .
Up there so high . . . touching the sky.
Old mem'ries desert me like clouds drifting by
And echo your last sad goodbye.

With friends and relations I'll go to the station
And try to pretend that I'm glad.
I'll hold your hand, darlin' . . . you'll understand,
I don't want them to know that I'm sad.

CHORUS:
Still every night when I turn out the light,
I dream of good times that have been.
But with the dawn I wake up and you're gone
And my heart breaks all over again.

CHORUS:

❖ *"Ragtime Annie" is the theme song of the Weiser Fiddle Contest and if you want to hear variation in a traditional tune take in the contest and hear a* *hundred different fiddlers put their signature on this well known piece.*

—R.S.

RAGTIME ANNIE

I met Manny Shaw at the Weiser Fiddle Contest back in the late fifties. He has a jamboree over in Fairfield every year and keeps a museum filled with memories of Idaho fiddling. He brought a troop of storytellers, singers and his fiddle to our Idaho City concert and gave us a solid contribution for our project. (Photo courtesy of Michael Cordell)

Muzzy Braun — one of a family of working Idaho musicians. A singer-songwriter, performer, father and the possessor of boundless energy . . . a good man to be in charge "At An Idaho Dance."
(Photo courtesy of Michael Cordell)

218

❖*This is a dance call—delivered like a sermon to a lively fiddle tune at an Idaho cowboy dance. I found it in a newspaper clipping titled, "Old Dad's Scrap Book."* —R.S.

OLD DAD'S SCRAPBOOK
Anonymous

Git yo' little sage hens ready, trot 'em out upon the floor;
Line up there, you cusses; steady, lively now, one couple more.
Shorty, shed that old sombrero; Bronco, douse that cigarette;
Stop that cussin', Casimero, 'fore the ladies. Now all set!

S'lute your ladies all together, ladies opposite the same;
Hit the lumber with your leathers, balance all an'
   swing your dame.
Bunch the heifers to the middle, circle stag and do-se-do;
Pay attention to the fiddle, swing her round and off you go!

First four forward, back to your places; second follow,
   shuffle back;
Now you've got it down to cases, swing 'em till your
   trotters crack.
Gents all right, a-heel-and-toeing. Swing 'em, kiss 'em
   if you kin;
On to next and keep a-goin' till you hit your pards again!

Gents to center, ladies round 'em; form a circle, balance all.
Whirl your gals to where you found 'em, promenade around
   the hall.
Balance to your pards and trot 'em round the circle double quick,
Grab and kiss 'em while you've got 'em, hold 'em to it if
   they kick!

Ladies, left hand to your sonnies, alamain, grand right and left;
Balance all and swing your honeys, pick 'em up and feel
   their heft.
Promenade like skeery cattle, balance all and swing your sweets;
Shake yer spurs and me 'em rattle, Kino! Promenade to seats!

David Sealander calls his farm near Idaho Falls, "New Sweden." The first time I heard him, he introduced me to the "hardangar" fiddle and the special joy that shines in Swedish music. You can see it for yourself in his smile or hear it for yourself when David organizes a music function in eastern Idaho. (Photograph by Michael Cordell)

❖This tune was composed to commemorate the earthquake that shook everything for miles around Challis in 1983.   —R.S.

MACKAY STOMP

Written by Will Welling

Glen Taylor and the Glendora Singers. (Photo courtesy of Idaho State Historical Society)

❖ *This was written in 1980 about a community party held every winter to fight cabin fever. Muzzy Braun is one of a whole family of working musicians in Idaho. The Braun Brothers—Muzzy, Gary, and Billie are favorites all over the state—each equally loved as singles. Muzzy's sons—the Little Braun Brothers—are fast becoming a national treasure. This song really captures the influence of Bob Will's fiddle style on our western music.*

—R.S.

IDAHO SWING

Written by Muzzy Braun

Here it is a-gain Saturday night And the band is playin' swing.

Ev-'ry-bo-dy got a gal whirl-in'-a round. And I love to watch 'em dance 'n swing.

Hard-wood floor and a bot-tle o' beer, You're in Id-a-ho, that's for sure.

Get-tin' real loose at the Smi-ley Creek Lodge, Goin' to

dance til your feet get sore. Swing! Dance that I-da-ho swing. I said

sing, I love to watch 'em shake that thing. I said *whirl*, why don't you

give that gal a whirl? Ev-'ry-bo-dy stop, drink up your cup, We're goin' to

dance til the sun comes up.

IDAHO SWING
By Muzzy Braun

Here it is again Saturday night
And the band is playing swing.
Everybody got a gal whirlin' around
And I love to watch 'em dance and swing.
Hardwood floor and a bottle of beer,
You're in Idaho, that's for sure.
Gettin real loose at the Smiley Creek Lodge,
Goin to dance til your feet get sore.

Swing! Dance that Idaho swing.
I said *sing*, I love to watch 'em shake that thing.
I said, *whirl*, why don't you give that gal a whirl?
Everybody stop, drink up your cup,
We're goin dance til the sun comes up.

Saturday night and the barroom's jammed,
All the local folks came to dance.
Slap back a beer, grab up a gal,
Get out and take a chance.
You know it don't take long to learn
The moves you can do in an hour or so.
Dancin and drinkin at the Smiley Creek Lodge
In Sawtooth City, Idaho.

Swing! Dance that Idaho swing.
I said *sing*, I love to watch 'em shake that thing.
I said, *whirl*, why don't you give that gal a whirl?
Anybody here tonight from Idaho?
Why don't you stand up and let us know.

Here it is again Saturday night
And the band is playing swing.
Everybody got the gal whirling around,
I love to watch 'em dance and swing.
Well there's a few more moves than when your
  daddy was here
But the night always turns out right.
Still drink beer and have a hell of a time
Dancin on a Saturday night.

I'm talking swing, dance that Idaho swing.
I said *sing*, I love to watch 'em shake that thing.
I said, *whirl*, why don't you give that gal a whirl?
Well everybody stop, drink up your cup,
We're goin dance until the sun comes up!

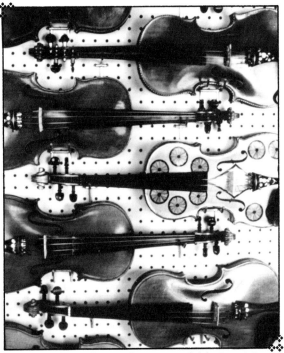

Manny Shaw fiddle collection.(Photo courtesy of Idaho Commission on the Arts)

White Cloud Mountains.(Photo courtesy of Ernest E. Day)

PASSING THROUGH

S O N G S H O M E M A D E & H O M E S U N G

I saw Adam leave the garden with an apple in his hand.
I said, "Now you're out, what are you gonna do?"
"Plant my crops and pray for rain, maybe raise a little Cain . . .
I'm an orphan and I'm only passing through."

Dick Blakeslee

Opal Brooten of Coeur d'Alene sang "Passing Through" to us. She learned it at the Idaho Progressive Party Convention at Lewiston in 1948 when Henry Wallace was running for President with Idaho Senator Glen Taylor as his running mate. I have heard the song used for all kinds of political rallies — the singers changing it to fit the time and place. It's one of those tools people use when the need arises . . . easy to learn and stirring — it brings people together in a common cause — makes one powerful voice out of many. This last section contains songs that are contemporary — home-made and home-sung. The process goes on — all the hype and hard-sell in the world cannot stop the human impulse to make a song when it's needed or to sing it when it's time.　　—R.S.

PASSING THROUGH

As Sung by Opal Brooten
Written by Dick Blakeslee

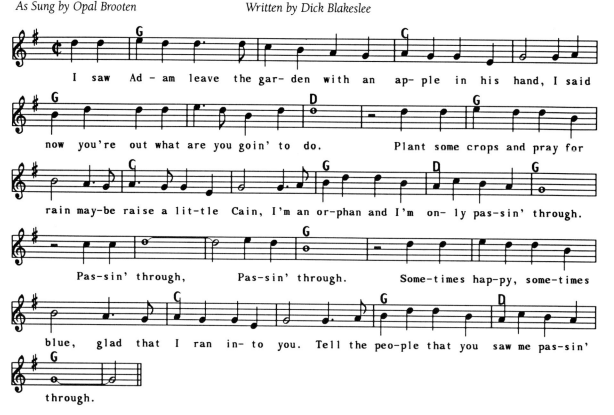

I saw Adam leave the garden with an apple
  in his hand
I said, "Now you're out what are you going to do?"
"Plant some crops and pray for rain, maybe raise
  a little Cain,
I'm an orphan now and only passing through."

CHORUS:
Passing through, passing through,
Sometimes happy, sometimes blue,
Glad that I ran into you,
Tell the people that you saw me passing through.

I saw Jesus on the cross on that hill called Calvary
"Do you hate mankind for what they've done
  to you?"
He said, "Talk of love not hate — things to do
  it's getting late,
I've so little time and I'm only passing through."

CHORUS:
I shivered next to Washington one night at
  Valley Forge,
"Why do the soldiers freeze here like they do?"
He said, "Men will suffer, fight, even die for
  what is right,
Even though they know they're only passing
  through."

CHORUS:
Was at Franklin Roosevelt's side just a while
  before he died.
He said, "One world must come out of World
  War II,
Yankee, Russian, White, or Tan, Lord, a man is
  just a man,
We're all brothers and we're only passing through."

CHORUS:
I saw Truman's Cold War plan, saw Korea and
  Viet Nam.
Shall we work for peace or make more
  bombs for war?
Shall we send our sons to fight for the rich man's
  power and might,
Or shall we stop their plans for nuclear war?

Passing through, passing through,
Sometimes happy, sometimes blue,
Glad that I ran into you,
Hope you hear my voice as I am passing through!

John Thompsen lives up the road from me on Moore's Creek with his wife, Ruth, who brings the Bookmobile around to the most remote corners of Boise County, and his two children. He is a talented woodworker and one of my favorite singers . . . often seen with the fine Moore's Creek String Band. (Photo courtesy of Michael Cordell)

❖ *This song is from John Thomsen of Idaho City. John wrote this for a skit put on in Idaho City recently. It is a true story much told in our part of the country about the Pinkham-Patterson shootout at Warm Springs outside of Idaho City in 1865.*

People love to make up songs about their outlaws and hard-cases. There are many current songs about Claude Dallas, *for example, and as you can see throughout this book, homage has been paid to every kind of criminal, from murderers to bank-robbers to politicians. When I asked my friend Olive Wooley Burt why she was so fascinated by murder, she said, "That is a very passionate act for a human being to commit . . . one can't help wondering how and why things can come to such a pass."*

—R.S.

PINKHAM AND PATTERSON

Written by John Thomsen

In eight-een six-ty-five when dreams of gold were be-ing spun Ferd Pat-ter-son came rid-ing o'er the hills from Or-e-gon. A gam-blin' man, a Dem-o-crat and cham-pion of the south, and the kil-ler of a steam-boat cap-tain down at Col-um-bia's mouth. Sum-ner Pink-ham had been sher-iff in eight-een six-ty four, But the Dem-o-crats had won the vote and sent Pink out the door. For Pink-ham was Re-pub-li-can, staunch Un-ion man was he. He'd sing "We'll hang Jeff Da-vis from a sour ap-ple tree." Well one fine Sun-day eve-ning on Ju-ly the twen-ty third Down at the Warm Springs plunge Sum-ner met with drunk-en Ferd Pink sang a song which an-gered Ferd 'til Pat-ter-son saw red

and jerk-ing out his for-ty four shot Sum-ner Pink-ham dead. And

when he saw what he had done he threw his pis- tol down and

catch- ing up a near- by horse rode hard for Boi-se town. But

he was caught and cap- tured be - fore he'd gone too far, and

tak-en to the jail- house at Bue-na Vis-ta Bar. "Foul play" the vi-gi

lan- tes cried "We'll hang him from a tree." "Twas self de-fense" the

ju - ry said and Pat- ter- son went free. So Ferd rode off to

Wash- in- ton and in Wal- la Wal- la there He was shot and

killed while sit-ting in a bar- ber chair. Tis said that mu-sic

hath a charm to soothe the sa- vage breast, But one should use dis

cre-tion when sing-ing songs in jest Be - cause as Sum- ner

Pink-ham learned one Sun- day in the west mu-sic al- so has the

po - wer to charm a bul - let to your chest.

I wrote this song because we needed a 'huckleberry' song and could not find one. Also, I wanted to tell a story in song form about how much huckleberry picking is a part of not only my own family heritage but also the culture of the Silver Valley and North Idaho. People who live here enjoy a ride in the hills no matter what the season, but especially during the time when all members of the family, from the little ones to the seniors, gather the distinctive-tasting huckleberries. Families often have their favorite "patches," the locations of which are a carefully guarded secret.

Uncle Bill Etherton always scouted early and let us know where the best berries could be found. When his homemade, wooden huckleberry pack was "filled to the brim" we knew there would be a break from the summer doldrums — a ride in the mountains! On these trips we children learned about geology, plants, animals, and local history, but most of all we developed an appreciation for our environment which we are passing on to the next generation of little huckleberry pickers.

—Jackie Fields (Pinehurst)

UNCLE BILL'S HUCKLEBERRY SONG

Written by Jackie Fields

Sit-tin' in the sum-mer at the grand folks' place, Creek's too dry to swim

Here comes Un-cle Bill with a smile on his face and his ber-ry pack full to the

brim. Well we know right a-way that the ve-ry next day we'll be off at the crack of

dawn 'cause you've got-ta be quick and start to pick or the ber-ries will all be

gone _____, or the ber-ries will all be gone. Load up in the truck and

head up the hill Rid-ing in the mount-ains is the big-gest thrill.

Sit-tin' in the patch just eat-in' our fill pick-in' huck-le-ber-ries with my

Un-cle Bill

Sittin' in the summer at the grand folk's place,
Creek's too dry to swim
Here come Uncle Bill with a smile on his face
And his berry pack full to the brim

Well we know right away that the very next day
We'll be off at the crack of dawn 'cause you've
Gotta be quick and start to pick or the berries will all be gone, or the
Berries will all be gone.

CHORUS:
Load up the truck and head up the hill
Riding in the mountains is the biggest thrill
Sittin' in the patch just eat-in' our fill
Pickin' huckleberries with my Uncle Bill

See an old cabin all covered with Vines
Down the road are a couple-a old mines,
We all jump out, run around, explore
Jump back in and we drive some more.
We ask Uncle Bill about the flowers on the hill
'Cause he always knows what they are,
There he shows us trails and tells us tales,
So the trip doesn't seem so far,
So the trip doesn't seem so far

CHORUS:
When we finally stop we're upon the top,
And the view goes on for miles
Spindly trees in the Alpine breeze
And our faces all in smiles.
We eat our lunch and the whole darn bunch
Of us pick 'til our fingers turn blue.
Then it's home we go when the sun sinks low,
Uncle Bill's Huckleberrying crew,
Uncle Bill's Huckleberrying crew,

CHORUS:

❖ *The sincerity of this song reflects Idahoans'*
commitment to the environment. —R.S.

PCB SONG

Written by Jackie Fields

Right over the hill from me I can see P. C. B. Right over the hill from me I see P. C. B.'s There can-not be, we must be free from an-oth-er dead-ly tox-in. You can-not tell but you know darn well that it could be di-ox-in. Right over the hill from me I don't want to see an-y P. C. B. Right over the hill from me I don't want P. C. B. La la la la la la la la la la la la la la la la la la la la la la la la. So cut the gloss from Mis-ter Ross, 'cause we can see right through it. He'll have to learn that he can't burn, we just won't let him do it. Right over the hill from you don't be blue, here's what we'll do Right over the hill from me, we will stop P. C. B.'s we will stop P. C. B.'s We stopped P. C. B.'s!

232

I've had a good deal of fun with this song and have enjoyed hearing it sung by many different people. Of course, the song's hopelessly out of date. The AEC is now the INEL and "Ray Bans" (trade name for a brand of sunglasses) and "Gucci" have been super-seded by "Varnets" and "Ocean Pacific." The reference to the bunnies at Mud Lake is an illusion to the jack rabbit roundups in Eastern Idaho. The rabbit popula-tion had exploded and was eating up cattle fodder.

—Johnny Thomsen

IDAHO SPUD
(To the Tune of "Tennessee Stud")

Along about nineteen-seventy-four,
I left Sun Valley, it was such a bore . . .
I hocked my Ray Bans and Gucci duds
And I went out to dig me an Idaho Spud.

I motored on down into Burley town . . .
Found a cute little russet sorta knobby and brown
I said, "Sweet thing, I'll dig you later,
Right now I'm gonna dig me an Idaho 'tater.'"

CHORUS:
The Idaho spud was long and green,
Covered with the butter and the sour cream . . .
Dig it from the ground and clean off the mud . . .
There never was a 'tater' like the Idaho spud.

You eat them lobsters on the coast of Maine,
Eat the gila monster on the Texas plain . . .
Black man down under eats the wichity grub,
And it all goes better with an Idaho spud.

You can make it into vodka, make it into beer,
You can eat it with a chicken or an old dead steer
Stopper up a gas tank, serve it in a club . . .
Nothin' goes better than an Idaho spud.

CHORUS

You got your nuclear waste on the desert floor
And the AEC wants to ship in more . . .
Big hole in the ground where they're droppin'
    their crud . . .
Radio-active Idaho spud.

I got a cute little mutant on the cabin floor
And another half a kid just to stop the door . . .
They light right up like green tomaters
Feedin' my kids them nuclear 'taters.'

2nd CHORUS:
The Idaho spud glows long and green . . .
Use it in a bomb or run a submarine . . .
You can nuke them bunnies down at old Mud Lake,
But don't go messin' with my Irish steak.

(Alternate last line: A little bit later we're all
    gonna glow eatin' them 'taters' from Idaho.)

REPEAT CHORUS

❖ *This song was inspired by Representative George Hansen's campaign comic book, (entitled "George The Dragon Slayer") and the old rumor that "Puff the Magic Dragon" was a drug song about marijuana* ("Puff the magic drag in," you know.) *The song was written by Paul Menser, a newspaper man from Idaho Falls. Journalists have often been the best purveyors of parody.*

—R.S.

GEORGE THE DRAGON SLAYER
(To the tune of "Puff the Magic Dragon")
By Paul Menser

George the Dragon Slayer was a big man,
Whether or not you wanted to, he'd try to shake your hand.
He would put down dragons with words both grim and gruff,
And in the course of his crusade he vowed to do in Puff.

CHORUS:
Oh! George, the Dragon Slayer was a big man,
Whether or not you wanted to he'd try to shake your hand.

Puff was oft reputed to be stoned out on pot.
Allegations of this sort made Big George mighty hot.
With his sword a-sharpened he set off for Puff's lair,
His boasting of his prowess made him late in getting there,

CHORUS

Puff, he quaked with terror when he saw George's knife.
He knew he would have to plead if he would save his life.
So he made an offer which Big George thought quite fair:
"Put away your sword and I'll supply you with hot air."

CHORUS

GOVERNOR BLEW HIS STACK:
SONG HELPED SAVE WHITE CLOUD PEAKS
By Paul Swenson
(Desert News, 14 November, 1970)

When Depression songwriters squeezed the last drops of dry humor from the grapes of wrath in such songs as "Keep Moving" and "Whitehouse Blues," politicians drank the dregs.

President Herbert Hoover was harpooned in the latter tune ("Look here, Mr. Hoover/See what you done/You went off a' fishing/Let the country go to ruin"), and although the tone was light rather than bitter, the president would probably have had good reason to resent the implications.

Songs about social issues have a way of popping up in political campaigns, and now a tune composed by a former Utahn has figured into a gubernatorial race in Idaho.

The name of the song is "White Clouds." It is Rosalie Sorrels' personal expression of concern for preservation of the White Cloud Mountains wilderness in her native Idaho.

Although Miss Sorrels wrote the song as a protest against a proposal to permit open pit mining of molybdenum ore at the base of Castle Peak in the White Clouds — an operation which many conservationists fear would scar the natural beauty of the area — it was not intended as a political attack.

"White Clouds," in fact, contains a gentle and poetic appeal to a wider audience on a universal theme — the redemption of the American wilderness from pollution and commercial encroachment.

But when Stacy Gebhards, a wildlife biologist in the Idaho Fish and Game Department, began to sing the song in public with two friends early this year, he quickly got in trouble.

Gebhards and his friends performed at a state dinner last spring. Among those in attendance were Secretary of the Interior Walter G. Hickel and Idaho Governor Don Samuelson.

As the words to "White Clouds" filled the darkened auditorium, color slides of Idaho's pollution problems flashed on a screen.

Gebhards received a personal commendation and a congratulatory letter from Hickel. But the word from the governor's office was that if he ever sang the song in public again, he would be fired.

"The governor blew his stack," a political analyst for an Idaho newspaper told this writer. "He reacted as if it were an insult for anyone to suggest there might be such a thing as pollution in Idaho."

Open pit mining of the White Clouds became an issue in the gubernatorial campaign when Samuelson's challenger, Cecil Andrus, opposed the move. The governor campaigned on a promise to support the mining.

Andrus was the winner on November 3, and the pristine beauty of the White Clouds — not to mention Gebhard's job security — has presumably been preserved. . . .

WHITE CLOUDS

As Sung by Rosalie Sorrels

Written by Rosalie Sorrels

White Cloud Mountains.(Photo courtesy of Ernest E. Day)

This mountain reaches for the eagle's flight . . .
It lifts its head among white clouds . . .
Its song the wind, the thunder and the rain . . .
Its foot in flowers, its mantle green with trees that
    stand so proud.

And would you see the mantle fall?
Cut down and lying dusty on the ground?
The song become the roar of trucks, the whine of steel?
The eagle flown, the White Clouds stained a dirty brown?

"It's such a little part of all we have," they say . . .
"We'll put it back the way it was when we have done . . .
And we'll have money for those thousand things we need . . .
And we'll replace each fallen tree, each broken stone,
    each uptorn weed."

Oh who has seen the way we rape our land?
From Kentucky's green hills to the San Francisco bay . . . ?
And who has put it back the way it was?
And who has shared the spoils, the way they say?

This mountain reaches for the eagle's flight . . .
It lifts its head among white clouds . . .
Its song the wind, the thunder and the rain . . .
Its foot in flowers, its mantle green with trees that
    stand so proud.

Through the years, the United Farm Workers patiently organized the rich farmlands of California, moving northward through the vineyards, southward through the vegetable and fruit lands, attracting national attention with their grass-roots democracy and their dedication to nonviolence.

Excluded by law from the protection of the National Labor Relations Board, the Farm Workers depended on publicity and on boycotts to make their point. Finally, in 1970, the growers agreed to recognize the union.

By the end of the 1970s, despite the attempts of some growers to divide the farm workers with interunion jurisdictional disputes, the United Farm Workers won collective bargaining rights in California, higher wages, and better living conditions. But outside of California, pickers have as little as ever. Today, fewer than 10 percent of the farm workers in America have any union protection.

The theme song of the most militant strike of the last quarter-century speaks only of the colors and sounds of the earth, which are everyone's birthright.

—Pete Seeger and Bob Reiser
(*Carry It On!* 1985)

❖The Boise Peace Quilt Project, a company of women who honor people of peace with hand-made, heart-felt quilts, awarded Ceasar Chavez a beauty. When he came to accept it there was a wonderful celebration which included traditional food and music. As the quilt was being presented, the band began to play "De Colores," the anthem of la Huelga — the United Farm Workers' struggle for human rights. It made my heart swell with pride when almost everyone in the room began to sing along with the band. When I first became aware of the struggle in the early seventies, the people of Idaho were not receptive to the work of this great Mexican-American hero. —R.S.

DE COLORES
Traditional

De co-lo-res, de co-lo-res se vis-ten los cam-pos en la pri-ma ver-ra. De co-lo-res, de co-lo-res son los pa-ja ri-tos que vie-nen dea-fue-ra. De co-lo-res, de co lo-res es el ar-co i-ris que ve-mos lu-cir; Y por e-so los gran-des a mo-res de mu-chos co-lo-res me gus-tan a-mi; Y por e-so los gran-des a mo-res de mu-chos co-lo-res me gus-tan a-mi.

Cesar Chavez, United Farm Workers. (Photograph by Victor Aleman)

DE COLORES (IN COLORS)

De colores, de colores se visten los Campos en la prima vera
De colores, de colores son los pajaritos que vienen deafuera.
De colores, de colores es el arco iris que vemos lucir;
Y por eso los grandes a-mo-res de muchos colores me gustan a mí;

Canta el gallo, canta el gallo con el quiri- quiri-quiri-quiri-quiri;
La gallina, la gallina con el cara-cara-cara- cara-cara;
Los polluelos, los polluelos con el pío-pío- pío-pío-pío;
Y por eso los grandes amores de muchos colores me gustan a mí;
Y por eso los grandes amores de muchos colores me gustan a mí.

In colors, in colors the fields in the spring dress up.
In colors, in colors the little birds come from far off.
In colors, in colors the rainbow we see glistening;
And that's why those big many-colored loves are what I like.

The rooster, the rooster sings with his cock-a- doodle-a-doodle-a-doo;
The hen, the hen with cackle-a-cackle-a-cackle-a-cack;
The chicks, the chicks with their cheepy-cheepy-cheepy-cheep;
And that's why those big many-colored loves are what I like.

239

(*Photograph by Jan Boles*)

This song kind of sums up all these things that happened in the West after the Civil War. It's a boomer's song about silver mining, about farming, about cattle ranching, with the recurring refrain, "I guess she'll never be mine," but with the final statement, "I've won all her treasures so simple and fine, and I know some day she'll be mine."

That's what union organizing, or any kind of organizing, is supposed to be for: to help working people, no matter what their trades, to reach out toward each other, to sit down together and define their problems, define their solutions, and then to get to work on it and begin to get back some of the wealth they have created over the years.

This is a love song. It's my love song for the country I come from. I've tried to include in it a lot of the ways I know other people feel about it too.

—Utah Phillips

SHE'LL NEVER BE MINE

Written by Bruce "Utah" Phillips

My love is a river where the white waters pour,
I've hunted and trapped her through
the gates of Leadore.
She sings through a curtain of cold mountain rain,
Where I dug her bright silver in the
high Coeur d'Alenes.

CHORUS:
She'll never be mine, she'll never be mine.
I've won all her treasures so simple and fine,
But I know she'll never be mine.

My love is a cantina where I drink with my friends
I've called her Delores and sometimes Cheyenne.
I've followed her begging all over the West . . .
My love is a headlight on the midnight express.

CHORUS:
My love is Montana and the high Douglas fir . . .
Many long summers I've labored for her . . .
My love is the windrows of dry autumn corn
That grow on the land where my children were born.

CHORUS:
My love is the life that a boomer will lead . . .
But you've bought her with lies and chained her
with greed . . .
My love is a dreamer . . . I'll follow the dream . . .
You say she's a beggar . . . I say she's a queen.

2nd Chorus:
Some day she'll be mine . . . Some day
she'll be mine.
I've won all her treasurers so simple and fine,
And I know some day she'll be mine.

SUGGESTED READING

RESOURCES

There are a number of folklore and oral history collections in the state and the region. The following collections are simply suggested as a place to begin looking for additional information:

The Idaho State Historical Library in Boise

The Idaho Folklife Archives at ISHS

The Folk Art of Idaho Collection, Idaho Commission on the Arts, Boise

Latah County Historical Society, Moscow

North Idaho Oral History Collection, Coeur d'Alene

Ketchum Community Library, Ketchum

Idaho Perspectives Collection, Shoshone City Library, Shoshone

Randall V. Mills Memorial Archive of Northwest Folklore: University of Oregon, Eugene, Oregon

Fife Folklore Archive: Utah State University, Logan, Utah

BIBLIOGRAPHIES AND INDEXES:

Austin, Judith and Gary Bettis, "A Preliminary Checklist of Guides to Sources of Idaho History," *Idaho Yesterdays* 21(1977): 19-26.

Buckendorf, Madeline and Elizabeth P. Jaycox, *Directory of Oral History Resources in Idaho,* Boise: Idaho Oral History Center, Idaho State Historical Society, 1982. *Idaho Local History: A Bibliography with Checklist of Library Holdings,* Moscow: University of Idaho Press, 1976.

Lawless, Elaine, *Guide to Idaho Folklore Archives,* Idaho State Historical Society, n.d.

McCarl, Robert S. and JaNene Buckway, eds., *Shoshone and Idaho Perspectives* (Boise: Idaho Commission on the Arts and the Lincoln County Centennial Committee, 1989)

Mercier, Laurie, Carole Simon-Smolinski, eds., and Bobbi Rahder and Mary Reed, *Idaho's Ethnic Heritage: A Resource Guide,* Boise: Idaho Ethnic Heritage Project — Idaho Centennial Commission, National Park Service, and the U.S. Department of the Interior. 1990.

——————. *Idaho's Ethnic Heritage: Historical Overviews, Volume 1 and 2,* Boise: Idaho Ethnic Heritage Project — Idaho Centennial Commission, the National Park Service and the U.S. Department of the Interior, 1990, and U.S. Department of the Interior

Rikoon, Sanford J. "An Annotated Bibliography of Materials on Idaho Folklife," in Louie Attebery, ed., *Idaho Folklife: Homesteads to Headstones.* Salt Lake City: University of Utah Press, 1985: 233-37.

Sevy, Jil, Index to Folk Art of Idaho, "We Came to Where We Were Supposed to Be," Survey of traditional arts in Idaho. Boise: Idaho Commission on the Arts. Guide to the collection on dBase III Plus program, 1989.

Siporin, Steve, editor, *We Came to Where We Were Supposed to Be. Folk Art of Idaho.* (Boise: Idaho Commission on the Arts, 1984.)

Stringfellow, Nancy and Beth A. Wilson, editors, *Bibliography of Early Boise Basin History* (Boise: Boise Public Library, 1983)

Walls, Robert E., editor and compiler, *Bibliography of Washington State Folklore and Folklife.* Seattle: University of Washington Press and Washington State Folklife Council, 1987.

Section I: We Were Always Here:
The Native People of Idaho

The most comprehensive and contemporary summary of resources can be found in *Idaho's Ethnic Heritage: A Resource Guide* and its companion volumes, *Idaho's Ethnic Heritage: Historical Overviews, Volumes 1 & 2*, compiled and edited by Laurie Mercier and Carole Simon-Smolinski and Bobbi Rahder and Mary Reed (Boise, Idaho: Idaho Centennial Commission, National Park Service, U.S. Department of the Interior, 1990). In the *Resource Guide*, the Native American material can be found on pages 162-213; in the *Historical Overview*, the Native American material can be found at the end of Volume 2, pages 1-18. Ethnographic accounts of Idaho Indians can be found in Deward Walker, *Indians of Idaho* (Moscow: University of Idaho Press, 1982); and Julian Steward, "The Great Basin Shoshonean Indians," in *Theory of Culture Change*, edited by Julian H. Steward (Urbana: University of Illinois Press, 1955). In addition to the Shoshone material quoted in the text, additional information about Native American music in Idaho can be found in Loran Olsen, "Native Music of the Northwest: A Collection of Slide Shows, Videotapes, and Motion Pictures Depicting Various Musical and Ceremonial Activities of Native People in the Pacific Northwest," Music Department, Washington State University, Pullman, Washington, 99164. Also see "Music," by Thomas Vennum, Jr., in *Great Basin, Handbook of the North American Indians*, volume editor, Warren L. D'Azevedo; general editor, William C. Sturtevant (Washington, D.C.: Smithsonian Institution Press, 1986), pp. 682-704. Information about individual tribes can be found in the booklet, *Idaho Indians, Tribal Histories* (Boise, Idaho: Idaho Centennial Commission, Native American Committee, n.d.). Also see Allen Slickpoo, *Noo Ne Me Poo* (Lapwai: Nez Perce Tribe of Idaho, 1973), and Whitney McKinney, *A History of the Shoshone Paiutes of the Duck Valley Reservation* (Sun Valley, Idaho: Institute of the North American West, 1983). Additional Readings: Ethnographic presentations — Harou Aoki, *Nez Perce Texts* (Berkeley: University of California Press, 1979); Sven Liljeblad, *The Idaho Indians in Transition: 1805-1960* (Pocatello: Idaho State University Museum, 1972)

Section II: We're Coming Idaho:
Settlers and Immigrants

One of the most comprehensive analyses of Idaho folksong can be found in Jan Harold Brunvand, "Folk Song Studies in Idaho," in Louie Attebery, ed., *Idaho Folklife: Homestead to Headstones* (Salt Lake City: University of Utah Press, 1985), pp. 37-45. Also see Barre Toelken, "Northwest Traditional Ballads," *Northwest Review* (Winter, 1962). See the three volumes on *Idaho's Ethnic Heritage*, compiled and edited by Mercier and Simon-Smolinski, listed above. Also see Michael M.J. Fischer's article, "Ethnicity and the Post-Modern Arts of Memory," in James Clifford and George E. Marcus, eds., *Writing Culture: The Poetics and Politics of Ethnography* (Berkley: University of California Press, 1986), pp. 194-233. A useful beginning point for locating and analyzing ethnic and immigrant folklore can be found in Barbara Kirshenblatt-Gimblett, "Studying Immigrant and Ethnic Folklore," in Richard M. Dorson, editor, *Handbook of American Folklore* (Bloomington, Indiana: Indiana University Press, 1983), pp. 39-47. For materials on ethnic folklore in Idaho, consult the "Guide to the Idaho Folklore Archives," Elaine Lawless, editor, (Boise, Idaho: Idaho Folklife Center and the Idaho State Historical Society, 1983) under the name or specific folklore form [legend, myth] of the ethnic group.

The Idaho Commission on the Arts (304 W. State in Boise, Idaho 83720) also has an extensive collection of research materials related to ethnic and traditional folk arts, in addition to the original materials collected for the Idaho Folksong Project. Support is currently being sought for compilation and indexing of these materials into one collection. Specific references to Afro-Americans in Idaho can be found in Mamie Oliver, *Idaho Ebony: Afro-American Presence in Idaho State History* (Boise: Idaho Centennial Commission, Ethnic Heritage Committee, 1990). Also see Sister M. Alfreda Elsesohn, *Idaho Chinese Lore* (Caldwell, Idaho: Caxton Printers, 1970).

Section III: Way Out in Idaho:
Braggers, Skinners, & Boomers

One of the most comprehensive collections of folk songs about and from this period can be found in "Folk Songs of Idaho and Utah," by Rosalie Sorrels, Folkways #FH 5343, 1961. In addition to the songs and introductory material by Rosalie, the annotation by Kenneth S. Goldstein provides an extremely useful survey of regional material. Also see, *Ballads of the Great West*, edited with commentary by Austin and Alta Fife (Palo Alto, California: American West Publishing Company, 1970); and "On the Trail to Idaho," in *Cowboy Songs and Other Frontier Ballads*, collected by John and Alan Lomax (New York: MacMillan, 1938). An excellent collection of regional lore and literature (although hard to find in print) is "Rendezvous, Songs and Stories of the Idaho Country," edited and compiled by Kim Stafford (Pocatello: Idaho State University [Volume 17: 1& 2], 1982). The work most often quoted here is Vardis Fisher's, *Idaho Lore* (Caldwell: Caxton Printers, 1939); also see Vardis Fisher, *Gold Rushers and Mining Camps of the Early West* (Caldwell: Caxton Printers, 1968); Richard E. Lingenfelter, Richard A. Dwyer and David Cohen, editors, *Songs of the American West* (Berkeley: University of California Press, 1968).

Section IV: Jack of All Trades:
Songs and Stories of Work

The material on occupational folklore is considerable, although most of the information collected will be found in journals. An overview of the entire range of literature about occupational folklore can be found in Archie Green, "Industrial Lore: A Bibliographic-Semantic Query," in *Working Americans: Contemporary Approaches to Occupational Folklife*, edited by Robert H. Byington, Smithsonian Folklife Studies Number 3 (Washington, D.C.: Smithsonian Institution Press, 1978), pp. 71-103. Specific information on occupational folklore in the west can be found in *Cowboy Poetry: A Gathering*, edited by Hal Cannon (Salt Lake City, Utah: G. M. Smith, 1985); *Cowboy Poetry from Utah: An Anthology*, edited and compiled by Carol A. Edison (Salt Lake City, Utah: Utah Folklife Center, 1985); and *Heaven on Horseback: Revivalist Songs and Verse in the Cowboy Idiom*, edited by Austin and Alta Fife, Western Texts Society Series Number 1 (Logan, Utah: Utah State University Press, 1970. Other works which deal with occupational folklore include Louie Attebery, "Rural Traditions of the Snake River Valley," *Northwest Folklore* 1:2 (1965), pp. 23-30; Joyce Horvath, "Mining Lore from Kellogg," *Western Folklore* 22: 4 (1965), pp. 286-287. Also see *A Treasury of Western Folklore* (New York: Crown Publishers, 1951) and *A Treasury of Railroad Folklore* (New York: Crown Publishers, 1953) edited by B.A. Botkin (and in the latter volume, co-edited with Alvin Harlow). Additional material on occupational folklore can be found in the Idaho Folklore Archives at the Idaho State Library, Boise and the Fife Folklore Archive at Utah State University, Logan, Utah. Also see Pete Seeger and Bob Reiser, *Carry it On! A History in Song and Picture of the Working Men and Women of America* (New York: Simon and Schuster, 1985) as a source for songs about work and working traditions.

Section V: Come All Ye Toiling Millions: Songs and Stories of Struggle

Material relating to songs and stories of solidarity and in particular to the Industrial Workers of the World can be found in *Rebel Voices: An I.W.W. Anthology*, Edited by Joyce Kornbluh (Chicago: Charles H. Kerr Publishing Company, 1988). Also see *History of the Labor Movement in the United States. Volume IV: The I.W.W., 1905-1917*, by Phillip S. Foner (New York: International, 1965); *Rebels in the Woods: The I.W.W. in the Pacific Northwest*, by Robert L. Tyler (Portland: University of Oregon Press, 1967); *Joe Hill*, by Gibbs Smith (Salt Lake City, Utah, 1969); John Greenway, *American Folksongs of Protest* (Philadelphia, Pennsylvania: University of Pennsylvania Press, 1953; and Archie Green, "John Neuhaus: Wobbly Folklorist," *Journal of American Folklore* 73 (1960), pp. 189-217. Steward Holbrook, *Holy Old Mackinaw-A Natural History of the American Lumberjack* (New York: MacMillan, 1939). Also see Edith Fowke and Joe Glazer, *Songs of Work and Freedom* (Chicago, Illinois: Doubleday, 1960).

Section VI: Jerusalem: The Spiritual Quest

One of the most complete collections of spiritual folk music in our region can be found in Austin and Alta Fife's *Heaven on Horseback: Revivalist Songs and Verse in the Cowboy Idiom* (Logan, Utah: Utah State University Press, 1970); also see the Fife's *Saints of Sage and Saddle: The Folklore of the Mormons* (Bloomington, Indiana: Indiana University Press, 1956). Larry Danielson has a more general discussion of folklore in religious groups in "Religious Folklore," in Eliot Oring, ed., *Folk Groups and Folklore Genres* (Logan, Utah: University of Utah Press, 1986), pp. 45-70. Also see the individual entries in the *Idaho Ethnic Heritage* volumes listed above and specific entries in *Symposium on Folk Religion*, edited by Don Yoder, *Western Folklore* 33 (1974), Special Issue. Also see Eileen Southern, *The Music of Black America: A History* (New York: W.W. Norton and Company, 1971); and Ruben M. Campos, *El Folklore y la Musica Mexicana* (Mexico: Talleres Graficos de la Nacion, 1928); Americo Paredes, *A Texas-Mexican Cancionero: Folksongs of the Lower Border* (Urbana: University of Illinois Press, 1976); Raphael Patai and others, *Studies in Biblical and Jewish Folklore* (Bloomington, Indiana: Indiana University Folklore Series, Number 13, 1960); and for a more comprehensive view of folk and religious traditions in this area regarding a specific holiday see John E. Baur's, *Christmas on the American Frontier, 1800-1900* (Caldwell: Caxton Printers, 1961).

Section VII: Idahoe-down: Local Music, Local Dance

Collections and analyses of folk music traditions range from the classical, scholarly works such as Bruno Nettl's *Folk and Traditional Music of the Western Continents* (Englewood Cliffs, New Jersey: Prentice-Hall, 1965), to more localized analyses of fiddle music as in Louie Attebery's, "The Fiddle Tune: An American Artifact," *Northwest Folklore* 2 (1967): 22-29. Thomas Cheney's "Folk Ballad Characteristics in a Present-Day Collection of Songs," in Louie Attebery, ed., *Idaho Folklife: Homesteads to Headstones* (Salt Lake City:

University of Utah Press, 1985), pp. 171-184. Numerous examples of a regional analysis of folk music materials can be found in Barre Toelken's *The Dynamics of Folklore* (New York: Houghton Mifflin, 1979), pp. 369-388. The concluding portions of each section of Mercier and Simon-Smolinski's *Idaho's Ethnic Heritage* volumes (previously cited) also contain recorded materials and music from each of the ethnic groups listed. Also see Lloyd Shaw, *Cowboy Dance, A Collection of Western Square Dances* (Caldwell: Caxton Printers, 1948).

Section VIII: Women of the West: Heroines, Hurdy-Gurdies, and Fashionable Women

Folklore studies by women and about women's folklore can be found in a special issue of the *Journal of American Folklore*, "Folklore and Feminism," 100: 398 (October-December, 1987). Also see Claire Farrer, ed.,*Women and Folklore: Images and Genres* (Prospect Heights, Illinois, Waveland Press, 1986); Rosan A. Jordan and Susan J. Kalcik, eds., *Women's Folklore, Women's Culture* (Philadelphia: University of Pennsylvania Press, 1985; and Marta Weigle, *Spiders and Spinsters: Women and Mythology* (Albuquerque: University of New Mexico Press, 1982). Also see Susan Armitage, "Women and Men in Western History: A Stereotypical Vision," *Western Historical Quarterly* 16 (1985): 380-395; Anne M. Butler, *Daughters of Joy, Sisters of Misery: Prostitutes of the American West, 1865-90* (Urbana: University of Illinois Press, 1985); Christiane Fischer, ed., *Let Them Speak for Themselves: Women in the American West, 1849-1900* (New York: E.P. Dutton, 1978); and Teresa Jordan, *Cowgirls: Women of the American West* (Garden City, New York: Doubleday, 1982). Also see Anne B. Cohen, *Poor Pearl, Poor Girl! The Murdered Girl Stereotype in Ballad and Newspaper* (Austin, Texas: AFS Memoir Services, Volume 58, 1973).

Section IX: I'm Gonna Tell: Songs for Grownup Kids and Children

There is a vast literature regarding children's folklore and folksongs. One of the earliest classics is Iona and Peter Opie, *Children's Games in Street and Playground* (Oxford: Oxford University Press, 1969). Also see Rogert D. Abrahams, *Jump-Rope Rhymes: A Dictionary*, American Folklore Society, Bibliography and Special Series, volume 20, Austin: University of Texas Press, 1969; and Roger D. Abrahams and Lois Rankin, editors, *Counting Out Rhymes: A Dictionary*, American Folklore Society, Bibliography and Special Series, volume 31, Austin: University of Texas Press, 1980. Additional references can be found in Bessie Jones and Bess Lomax Hawes, *Step it Down: Games, Plays, Songs and Stories from the Afro-American Heritage*, New York: Harper and Row, 1972; Mary Knapp and Herbert Knapp, *One Potato, Two Potato: The Secret Education of American Children*, (New York: W.W. Norton, 1976); Carl Withers, *A Rocket in My Pocket: The Rhymes and Chants of Young Americans* (New York: Henry Holt and Company, 1948). An excellent bibliographic overview of children's folklore can be found in Herbert Halpert, "Childlore Bibliography: A Supplement," *Western Folklore* 41 (1982): 205-228. A thorough treatment of the legend of Bigfoot can be found in Sanford Rikoon, "The Narrative of 'Chief Bigfoot': A Study in Folklore, History and World View," in Louie Attebery, ed, *Idaho Folklife: Homesteads to Headstones* Salt Lake City, Utah: Utah University Press, 1985: 199-215. Also see Layne Gellner Spencer, *And Five Were Hanged, and Other Historical Short Stories of Pierce, Idaho — The Roughest and Toughest in the West* (Caldwell: Caxton Printers, 1968).

Section X: Fiddlin at an Idaho Dance:
Swing and Stomp

The most comprehensive collections of folksongs can be found in Russell Ames, *The Story of American Folksong* (New York: Grossett and Dunlap, 1955); Bruno Nettl, *An Introduction to Folk Music in the United States* (Detroit: Wayne State University Studies, number 7, paperback edition 1960, revised by Helen Myers in 1976); and the classic, historical work, D.K. Wilgus, *Anglo American Folksong Scholarship Since 1898* (New Brunswick, New Jersey: Rutgers University Press, 1959). More localized studies can be found in Jan Harold Brunvand, "Folksong Studies in Idaho," *Western Folklore* 24 (1965): 231-248; Barre Toelken, "Northwest Traditional Ballads: A Collector's Dilemma," *Northwest Review* 5 (1962): 9-17; Toelken, "Traditional Fiddling in Idaho," *Western Folklore* 24 (1965): 259-262; and Polly Stewart, "Retention and Change in the Singing Tradition of a Northern Idaho Family," in Louie Attebery, ed., *Idaho Folklife: Homesteads to Headstones* (Salt Lake City: University of Utah Press, 1985): 110-119; and Louie Attebery, "The Fiddle Tune: An American Artifact," *Western Folklore* 2 (1967): 22-29.

Section XI: Passing Through:
Songs Homemade and Home Sung

General collections include Olive Wooley Burt, *Murder Ballads and Their Stories* (New York: Oxford University Press, 1958); John Greenway, *American Folksongs of Protest* (Philadelphia: University of Pennsylvania Press, 1953); Lester Hubbard, *Ballads and Songs from Utah* (Salt Lake City, Utah: Utah University Press, 1961); Oscar Brand, *The Ballad Mongers* (New York: Funk and Wagnalls, 1962); Richard Reuss, "American Folksongs and Left-Wing Politics: 1935-1956," *Journal of the Folklore Institute* 12 (1975): 89-111; and Jens Lund and R. Serge Denisoff, "The Folk Music Revival and the Counter Culture: Contributions and Contradictions," *Journal of American Folklore* 84 (1971): 394-405. Also see John I. White, *Git Along Little Dogies: Songs and Songmakers of the American West* (Urbana: University of Illinois Press, 1975); and Austin and Alta Fife, *Ballad of the Great West* (New York: Clarkson Potter, 1969).

PERMISSIONS ACKNOWLEDGEMENTS

Grateful acknowledgment is made to the following contributors for permission to print or reprint material copyrighted or controlled by them. Performers who contributed their version of a traditional or original work have been credited with the rights to that work in this publication. Copyrighted material remains the property of the copyright holder regardless of its publication in this book.

Lawrence Aripa's "Coyote Story" is published here for the first time. Copyright © 1991 by Lawrence Aripa, Plummer, Idaho.

William H. Avery's "In Defense of Polygamy" is published here for the first time. Copyright © 1991 by William H. Avery, Plummer, Idaho.

"Dig Me a Grave in the Owyhees" by **Bud Baltazor** from *Last of the Mustangs and Jerkline Skinners*. Copyright © 1976 by Bud Baltazor. Reprinted with permission of Jerry Baltazor, Shoshone, Idaho.

"Early Morning Roundup" by **Owen Barton** from *Saddle Talk*. Copyright © 1985 by Owen Barton, Rogerson, Idaho.

Dick Blakeslee's "Passing Through" is published here for the first time. Copyright © 1991 by Dick Blakeslee.

Helen Blume's "The Tenderfoot" and "The Cowboy" are published here for the first time. Copyright © 1991 by Helen Blume, Challis, Idaho.

Anna Marie Boles' "More Pretty Girls Than One" is published here for the first time. Copyright © 1991 by Anna Marie Boles, Rock Creek, Idaho.

Muzzy Braun's "Idaho Swing" is published here by permission of the author. Copyright © 1980 by Muzzy Braun.

Jackie Brooks' "The Cannibal Song" is published here for the first time. Copyright © 1991 by Jackie Brooks, Caldwell, Idaho.

Opal Brooten's "The Story of Maggie Hall Known as Molly B'Dam," is published here for the first time. Copyright © 1991 by Opal Brooten, Wallace, Idaho.

Bryan Bundy's "A Game of Cards" and "Rissity Rassity" are published here for the first time. Copyright © 1991 by Bryan Bundy, Lewiston, Idaho.

Johnny Carrey's "Idaho Jack's Song," and "Lost Indian" are published here for the first time. Copyright © 1991 by Johnny Carrey, Riggins, Idaho.

Margaret Christian's "Ghigleri's Cannonball" is published here for the first time. Copyright © 1991 by Margaret Christian, Wallace, Idaho.

Maidell Clemets' "Miners and Muckers Together," and "The Second Battle of Bunker Hill" are published here for the first time. Copyright © 1991 by Maidell Clemets, Osburn, Idaho.

Rosphine Coby's "Grandma" is published here for the first time. Copyright © 1991 by Rosphine Coby, Fort Hall, Idaho.

Betty Corrigan's "Cowboy Jack" is published here for the first time. Copyright © 1991 by Betty Corrigan, Challis, Idaho.

Blanche Cowger's performances and versions of the following songs: "I Wish I Was Single Again," "The Gypsy's Warning," "Bad Brahma Bull" (Written by Curley Fletcher), "The Man Behind the Plow," "Little Sod Shanty on the Claim," "The Hobo's Song," "Starving to Death on a Government Claim," "A Drunkard's Ode," "Payday," and "God Does Not Compel Us to Go," are published here with permission of the performer/collector. Copyright © 1991 by Blanche Cowger, Kooskia, Idaho.

Linda Croft's "Neath the Crust of the Old Apple Pie" is published here for the first time. Copyright © 1991 by Linda Crofts, Burley, Idaho.

IDAHO
COMMISSION
ON THE ARTS
304 WEST STATE STREET
BOISE IDAHO 83720

Celebrate IDAHO
1890·CENTENNIAL·1990™

Generally known as "The Travelin' Lady," Rosalie Sorrels has been delighting regional, national, and international audiences with her one-woman performances for three decades. Her group performances with such folk legends as Ramblin' Jack Eliot, Malvina Reynolds, and Utah Phillips have also received rave reviews in places like The Boston Globe, The Village Voice, and The New York Times. Sorrels has seventeen albums and tapes to her credit, including Lonesome Roving Wolves (1980), Miscellaneous Abstract Record #1 (1982), Then Came the Children (1984), and Careful, There's a Baby in the House (1991). A Clearing in the Forest is scheduled for release on the Green Linnett label in April. Sorrels is also a gifted storyteller who makes regular appearances at annual gatherings like the National Storytelling Festival in Jonesborough, Tennessee. For two years, however, at the request of the Idaho Centennial Commission and the Idaho Commission on the Arts, she toured her home state to gather and compile the material in this volume. She has previously edited two books: What, Women, and Who, Myself I Am (1974) and Report from Grimes Creek After a Hard Winter (1990). Her honors and awards include a University President's Award for Western Life and Letters from Boise State University (1985), a Governor's Award for Excellence in the Arts (1986), and the Kate Wolf Memorial Award (1991). She makes her home in the cabin her father built near Boise, Idaho.

❖❖❖

Robert McCarl is the Folk Arts Director at the Idaho Commission on the Arts. He has worked primarily with occupational and ethnic groups in the development of public folklore projects.

❖ ❖ ❖

C   O   L   O   P   H   O   N

WAY OUT IN IDAHO

Designed by Shelley McCarl
Boise, Idaho
Composed by Image Projections
in Berkeley Old Style
Cover separation by Vivi-Color, Inc.
Cincinnati, Ohio

❖ ❖ ❖